ST...

You're ...
rarely ... about wrong.
Friends are amazed that you
can always talk your way out of
trouble. You care about things
deeply, but don't often let
others know as you're a very
private person.

Are you a collector?

no

yes

CIRCLE

Little Miss Friendly, that's
you. You're always the centre
of attention, with silly stories
and jokes to tell. Yet friends
know they can talk to you if
there's something on their
minds. You're also an animal
lover with lots of pets.

Do you always finish what you start?

no

yes

no

HEART

A bit of a softy, that's how
friends describe you, but
you won't let people take
advantage of your kind nature.
You're a very thoughtful
person, who can come up with
great ideas to make friends
feel special. And you never
forget a birthday.

You prefer mornings to evenings. True?

yes

yes

£6.65

WHAT'S IN...

p10

p17

p50

p108

Printed and published in Great Britain by
D.C. THOMSON & CO., LTD.,
185 Fleet Street, London EC4A 2HS.
© D.C. THOMSON & CO., LTD., 2004.
While every reasonable care will be
taken, neither D. C. Thomson & Co.,
Ltd., nor its agents accept liability for
loss or damage to colour transparencies
or any other material submitted to this
publication.
ISBN 0 85116 849 3

Some stories may have been previously published.

Cindy Lou lived with her dad, step-mum and two step-sisters. One weekend —

HEY, CINDY, WE'VE JUST SEEN THE NEW FAMILY FROM NEXT DOOR.

REALLY? WHAT ARE THEY LIKE?

WELL WE ONLY ... ONE OF THEM — ...'T WE, TONI?

YEA! HE'S THE S... ...D HE'S GORG...

Once Upon A Time...

SO I THINK IT'S TIME TO BE NEIGHBOURLY, EH?

KEEP YOUR CLAWS OFF HIM! I SAW HIM FIRST.

SO? HE'S HARDLY LIKELY TO LOOK AT YOU WHEN I'M AROUND!

ACTUALLY, IF YOU WANT MY OPINION HE'S AS GOOD AS MINE.

IF HE HAS ANY SENSE HE WON'T HAVE ANYTHING TO DO WITH EITHER OF THEM! BUT I'D BETTER NOT SAY SO.

And, soon —

QUICK! GET THIS PLACE TIDIED UP, CINDY. DAVID'S POPPING ROUND IN HALF AN HOUR.

DAVID?

YES! DAVID PRINCE FROM NEXT DOOR! WE DON'T WANT HIM THINKING WE LIVE IN A PIG STY.

YOU COULD GIVE ME A HAND THEN. MUM SAID WE *ALL* HAD TO TIDY UP.

WE CAN'T POSSIBLY HELP. WE HAVE TO GO AND GET OURSELVES READY.

YES, WE'VE GOT TO LOOK OUR BEST. YOU CAN TIDY THE ROOM, CINDY. YOU'RE GOOD AT THAT SORT OF THING.

TYPICAL. THEY *NEVER* HELP. BUT I SUPPOSE I'D BETTER MAKE AN EFFORT!

SOMETIMES I THINK MY SISTERS TAKE ME FOR GRANTED. I FEEL LIKE A REAL LIFE CINDERELLA — BUT WITHOUT THE FAIRY GODMOTHER.

SO TELL US ABOUT YOURSELF, DAVID. WHAT ARE YOUR HOBBIES?

WELL, FOOTBALL MAINLY AND . . .

OH, I LOVE FOOTBALL. MY LAST BOYFRIEND PLAYED AT SCRUM-HALF!

THAT'S A *RUGBY* POSITION.

YOU'RE RIGHT. AND — ER — WHO ARE YOU?

OH, SHE'S OUR STEPSISTER, CINDY LOU. GET US SOME DRINKS, WILL YOU, CINDY?

SO WHAT DO YOU THINK OF YOUR NEW PLACE, DAVID?

IT'S PRETTY COOL. I LIKE IT.

DAVID SEEMS REALLY NICE, BUT I BET THOSE TWO WON'T LET ME GET A LOOK IN.

Cindy was right —

'BYE, DAVID!

WE'LL SEE YOU SOON. POP ROUND ANY TIME.

'BYE, GIRLS. THANKS FOR THE DRINK, CINDY.

On Monday, as the girls made their way home from school —

EVERY GIRL IN CLASS IS DROOLING OVER DAVID. AND THOSE TWO JUST WOULDN'T LEAVE HIM ALONE. I'M FED UP HEARING HIS NAME ALREADY.

Then, at home —

OH, NO! ONE OF MY TRAINERS MUST HAVE FALLEN OUT OF MY BAG. I'D BETTER GO BACK AND SEE IF I CAN FIND IT.

But, at the door —

OH, GOOD BOY. YOU'VE FOUND MY SHOE AND BROUGHT IT TO ME.

WOW! THAT WAS LUCKY!

LET'S SEE WHO YOU ARE. THE TAG SAYS YOUR NAME IS BUTTONS AND . . . HEY, YOU LIVE NEXT DOOR.

Then —

OH, YOU'VE FOUND BUTTONS! I HOPE HE ISN'T CAUSING TROUBLE.

NO. IN FACT, HE FOUND MY LOST TRAINER, SO HE'S GOT ME OUT OF TROUBLE. WHY — WHY DON'T YOU BOTH COME IN FOR A MOMENT?

ACTUALLY, I HOPE YOU DON'T MIND, BUT I'VE WANTED TO SPEAK TO YOU EVER SINCE WE MET ON SATURDAY. IT'S JUST BEEN TOO DIFFICULT WITH YOUR SISTERS AROUND.

TELL ME ABOUT IT!

8

And they all lived happily ever after . . .

Oh, Baby!

There's nothing quite like pictures of baby animals for making us say "Awwww"! So here are some of our favourites – with a little bit of information, too.

PUPPY LOVE
These little cuties are 10 weeks old. King Charles II was said to own several of these little dogs.

BABY LONGLEGS
When a foal is born its legs are already 90% of their full-grown adult length.

PERFECT PETS
Lambs can make perfect pets – but they need quite a lot of looking after.

DEAR, DEER!
Most fallow deer, like the fawn seen here, are born in June and weigh around 4.5 kilos (10lbs).

TALL TAIL
Although a guinea-pig appears to have no tail, it does have a very, very small tail bone.

PERKY PIGS
Pigs and piglets are generally very clever and can be taught to do tricks — better than some dogs.

CUTE KITTIES
Like human babies, all kittens are born with blue eyes which change colour as they get older.

FUNNY BUNNIES
Baby bunnies are called kittens and, as they can be house-trained, make great indoor pets.

Makeover Magic!

Best friends, Amy and Maria, wanted to try new looks that were different from their usual jeans and jumpers! So we decided to give them the best ever makeover!

First of all a stylist provided us with a cool collection of trendy clothes. From these, the girls were allowed to choose their two favourite outfits and a party top.

Then, to finish, they had their hair and make-up done to go with each outfit! Wow! All of this left the two friends feeling fab - and looking fantastic!

You can judge the results on pages 82 and 100 - but first let's meet the lucky girls!

ALL ABOUT AMY

Born - 27.8.92

Family - Mum, Dad, brothers Alister and Robbie

Pets - dog, guinea pig, goldfish

Ambition - to be a singer

Fave colour - lilac

Fave food - chocolate, pasta

Loves - puppies

Hates - people being horrid to each other

What makes you grumpy - getting up early

What makes you happy - having lots of friends

ALL ABOUT MARIA

Born - 11.10.93

Ambition - to be a pop star

Family - Mum, Dad, brother Martin

Pets - guinea pig, hamster, goldfish

Fave colour - light blue

Fave food - Maltesers, apples

Loves - chocolate, my family

Hates - getting up in the morning, spiders

What makes you grumpy - friends being horrible

What makes you happy - hugs and kisses

Spring

The Comp

REDVALE COMP was looking for a novel fundraising idea —

WE WANT SOMETHING THAT EVERYONE CAN TAKE PART IN, SO GET THINKING. SEE WHO CAN COME UP WITH THE BEST SUGGESTIONS.

WE COULD HAVE A GRAND PRIZE DRAW . . . OR A SPONSORED SILENCE OR . . .

IDEAS BY THE END OF THE WEEK, PLEASE.

DON'T STRAIN YOUR BRAINS THINKING, GIRLIES. MY IDEA'S *SURE* TO BE CHOSEN!

YOU CERTAINLY HAVE PLENTY TO SAY, GAVIN. PITY IT'S ALL HOT AIR. HA, HA, HA!

But —

HOW ABOUT MEETING AFTER SCHOOL TO PUT TOGETHER SOME IDEAS?

SORRY, BECKY, I HAVE A DENTIST APPOINTMENT.

AND I'M GOING TO HOSPITAL TO VISIT THE LITTLE GIRL FROM NEXT DOOR. SHE'S DEAD EXCITED COS ONE OF THE BIG BROTHER CELEBS IS GOING ROUND THE WARD THIS AFTERNOON.

COOL! GET US AN AUTOGRAPH IF YOU CAN, LAURA?

BAD LUCK, BECKS. BUT I'LL LET YOU HELP OUT WITH MY IDEA — IF YOU'RE NICE TO ME, THAT IS.

DON'T HOLD YOUR BREATH, GAVIN.

On the way home —

JUST THINK, BECKY, LAURA MIGHT BE TALKING TO A TV STAR BY NOW.

WOW, BIG DEAL, HAYLEY. A BIG BROTHER CAST-OUT IS HARDLY CELEBRITY OF THE YEAR. LAURA WOULD HAVE BEEN BETTER HELPING ME THINK UP A FUND-RAISING IDEA TO . . .

. . . WAIT A MINUTE. THIS COULD BE GREAT! WE'D RAISE A FORTUNE — I KNOW WE WOULD.

WHAT'RE YOU ON ABOUT, BECKY? WHAT'S THE GREAT IDEA?

Later —

. . . THERE COULD BE THREE BOYS AND THREE GIRLS IN THE DOMESTIC BLOCK, AND THEY COULD DO TASKS TO EARN TREATS.

But Becky wouldn't say a word. At home —

SIX OF US COULD STAY IN AN ENCLOSED AREA WATCHED BY CLOSED CIRCUIT TV. PEOPLE COULD PAY A DONATION TO WATCH, THEN VOTE FOR THE PERSON THEY THINK SHOULD LEAVE — JUST LIKE ON TV.

COOL, BECKY! THE BOYS COULD BE MADE TO DO NEEDLEWORK — AND WASHING-UP! HAH!

16

IT'S A GREAT IDEA. I'M SURE EVERYONE WILL LOVE IT!

WELL, WE'LL FIND OUT WHEN I HAND IT IN TOMORROW. CAN YOU IMAGINE GAVIN PEELING SPUDS? HA, HA, HA! HE THINKS HE'S SO COOL.

Next day —

THERE WOULD BE A TEACHER IN THE BLOCK, OF COURSE. AND THE KIDS WOULD ALL GO HOME IN THE EVENING.

HMM, I THINK YOU MAY HAVE SOMETHING HERE, BECKY. BUT I'LL HAVE TO RUN IT PAST THE HEAD.

And at the next Assembly —

WE WILL BE HOLDING AUDITIONS AFTER SCHOOL TODAY, SO IF YOU WANT TO TAKE PART, YOU WILL HAVE TO CONVINCE THE SELECTION COMMITTEE TO CHOOSE YOU. THERE WILL BE THREE BOYS AND THREE GIRLS — ONE OF WHOM WILL BE BECKY SINDEN, AS IT WAS HER IDEA.

So —

WELL, HODGE, CONVINCE US. WHY DO YOU WANT TO BE A CONTESTANT?

ER — IT'LL RAISE A LOT OF MONEY, AND IT'LL BE A LAUGH. I THINK I'D FIT IN WELL COS I'M GAME FOR A LAUGH.

YEAH, THAT'S TRUE. HODGE MAY BE AN IDIOT — BUT HE IS A LAUGH!

Eventually —

SO THE CONTESTANTS WILL BE BECKY, ROZ CUMMINGS, VERA-JAYNE SMYTHE, DAVID HODGESON, GAVIN GREENE AND STUART LINTON.

OH, NO. WHY DID THEY GO FOR JAYNE THE PAIN? I VOTED FOR LAURA AS THE OTHER GIRL.

Outside —

IT'LL BE GREAT, GAV. AND THEY HAD TO CHOOSE US, DIDN'T THEY? AFTER ALL, IMAGE IS ALL-IMPORTANT WHEN PEOPLE ARE APPEARING ON TV.

IT'S ONLY CCTV, YOU BOZO, NOT NATIONAL NETWORK.

WILL THE PUBLIC BE VOTING FOR THE PERSON THEY WANT TO STAY, OR THE PERSON THEY WANT TO EVICT? D'YOU KNOW, GAV?

NOPE! BUT *I'LL* WIN, EITHER WAY. AND, BY THE WAY, *VERA*, THE NAME'S GAVIN, NOT GAV.

HAH! GAVIN MAY BE BIG-HEADED, BUT HE CERTAINLY CUT JAYNE THE PAIN DOWN TO SIZE.

MIND YOU, I FEEL A BIT AS IF THE TWO BIG-HEADS HAVE STOLEN MY IDEA! BUT I SUPPOSE IT DOESN'T REALLY MATTER, AS LONG AS WE MAKE MONEY.

HI, BECKY.

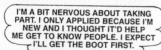

I'M A BIT NERVOUS ABOUT TAKING PART. I ONLY APPLIED BECAUSE I'M NEW AND I THOUGHT IT'D HELP ME GET TO KNOW PEOPLE. I EXPECT I'LL GET THE BOOT FIRST.

DON'T BE SO SURE, STUART. I KNOW WHO *I'D* VOTE OFF.

And, next day —

OH, NO! WHY DID IT HAVE TO BE THE BLIZZARD ON TEACHER DUTY FIRST? IT'D HAVE BEEN MORE FUN IF IT HAD BEEN SOOTY, OR TOSH.

CAMERAS ARE IN THE CORNERS — BUT NO POSING, PLEASE. THIS MORNING WE'LL ALL WORK TOGETHER TO PREPARE A MEAL — JUST LIKE IN A FOOD STUDIES LESSON.

HOW BORING.

AND THERE'LL BE NO SLACKING, JAYNE, OR YOU'LL ALL GET LINES TO DO INSTEAD OF FREE TIME THIS AFTERNOON.

BUT THAT'S NOT FAIR, I NEVER . . .

OH, STOP MOANING. THE QUICKER WE DO THE WORK, THE QUICKER WE GET TO PUT OUR FEET UP.

COME ON, GAVIN. YOU'RE ON SPUD PEELING WITH ME.

WHAT? WELL, I'M NOT WEARING THAT STUPID APRON!

Jayne wasn't happy either —

WATCH IT, PEA-BRAIN. THAT EGG'S GONE ALL OVER MY BLOUSE.

SORRY, I'M NOT MUCH GOOD AT THIS COOKING LARK! I'M BETTER AT CRACKING 'YOLKS'. HA, HA, HA!

Then —

WOOPS! CAREFUL, JAYNE.

WHAT D'YOU MEAN 'CAREFUL'? IT WAS YOU.

ALIEN ATTACK! BEWARE FLYING SAUCEPANS!

OH, SHUT UP, HODGE. AND — OH, NO! I'VE BROKEN A NAIL!

WOW! WHAT A DISASTER — NOT!

WOOPS! JAYNE WON'T LIKE THAT.

She didn't!

OH, PUSH OFF, GAVIN GREENE. YOU THINK YOU'RE SO GREAT, BUT YOU'RE RUBBISH! THERE'S NO WAY YOU'LL WIN THIS GAME.

WELL I'VE GOT MORE CHANCE THAN YOU! ALL YOU CARE ABOUT IS YOUR NAILS, YOUR HAIR AND YOUR CLOTHES. GET A LIFE, WILL YOU?

OKAY, I WILL — FAR AWAY FROM HERE! I'M SICK OF THIS STUPID GAME, ANYWAY. I'M LEAVING.

OH, NO! IF SHE LEAVES NOW IT'LL RUIN EVERYTHING!

19

Continued on page 53

What's your ideal pet?

Try our fun and funky quiz to discover your ideal animal pal!

1. How would you like to spend a perfect Saturday?

a) In bed
b) Going for a walk
c) Shopping
d) Hanging out with mates

2. Which of these best describes you?

a) Happy and cheerful
b) Sleepy and laid back
c) Energetic and sporty
d) Slightly shy, but funny

3. Choose your fave colour from those listed.

a) Blue
b) Purple
c) Yellow
d) Red

4. Which one of these soaps do you never like to miss?

a) Emmerdale
b) Hollyoaks
c) Coronation Street
d) EastEnders

5. Which of these exotic countries would you most like to visit?

a) Thailand
b) Australia
c) Mexico
d) Alaska

6. Choose the word you think sounds nicest.

a) Salubrious
b) Salmagundi
c) Salamander
d) Saltimbocca

7. Mmmm! Which of these sandwich fillings is the one for you?

a) Tuna
b) Ham
c) Peanut Butter
d) Egg

8. In The Four Marys, who's your favourite?

a) Simpy
b) Fieldy
c) Raddy
d) Cotty

9. Choose a number.

a) 2
b) 4
c) 8
d) 1

10. Which of these school subjects do you prefer?

a) English
b) Science
c) Geography
d) History

Conclusions:

33 – 40 Cat.
You're slightly lazy, so a low maintenance pet – like a proud and independent cat – would suit you perfectly. The two of you could spend happy hours crashed out in front of the TV or sunbathing in the garden. Bliss!

25 – 32 Dog.
You love to get out and about as much as possible, so a dog would be the ideal pet for you. Think of all the energetic ball games in the park, or the lovely long walks along the beach in summer. Perfect!

Now check out your answers.

1. a)4 b)2 c)3 d)1
2. a)2 b)4 c)3 d)1
3. a)1 b)2 c)4 d)3
4. a)4 b)1 c)2 d)3
5. a)3 b)4 c)2 d)1
6. a)4 b)2 c)1 d)3
7. a)2 b)3 c)1 d)4
8. a)4 b)3 c)2 d)1
9. a)2 b)3 c)4 d)1
10. a)2 b)4 c)1 d)3

17 – 24 Budgie.
A cheerful, chatty girl like you is always on the go, so your dream pet would be something which doesn't need too much looking after. How about a chirpy budgie? The two of you could chat happily for hours.

10 – 16 Rabbit.
Quiet and friendly, that's you, so you should choose a quiet and friendly pet - like a cute and cuddlesome little bunny! Awww! Cleaning out may not be huge fun, but your pet would certainly be Miss (or Mr) Cutesy!

Scarves and hats can be hung on hooks or draped over coat hangers.

Store your toiletries in a basket.

Stash stuff under your bed for instant tidiness! (Make sure it can't be seen!)

Throw out (or give away) anything you've not used or worn in the last year - you won't miss it!

time to

Is your room messy? Read on for our top tidying tips!

If you have a chair in your room don't leave things lying on it. It looks untidy.

Keep special stuff securely locked away.

Put dirty clothes in a laundry basket. Don't wait for Mum or Dad to do it!

Buy some posh boxes and store things in them.

Make your bed. It takes seconds but looks really good!

Use a bin - and empty it regularly!

Use separate drawers for socks, tights, undies, gloves, scarves, etc. Then you'll always be able to find them.

Use Blu Tack to stick posters to your wall, not Sellotape.

Keep all your magazines and books in a bookcase or on a shelf. If you're not going to read them again get rid of them.

Princess Penelope

Phone Susie!!!

(positively perfect in every way!)

tidy?

Ask Mum or Dad to put up some shelves!

Use one box or basket for fave nail varnishes.

Invest in a pinboard and use it to display special tickets, cards, programmes, etc.

Put CDs and cassettes back in their cases when you've finished listening to them. Then you'll always be able to find them.

Hang up all your coats and jackets until they're being worn again.

Dust or vacuum your room now and again.

Don't hang clothes on door handles. Put them inside your wardrobe on hangers. Then they won't be creased when you want to wear them!

TOP TUNES

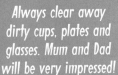

Only keep out the CDs and cassettes you listen to most. Keep the others out of sight in a drawer or box.

Always clear away dirty cups, plates and glasses. Mum and Dad will be very impressed!

Keep necklaces tidy but easy to reach by hanging them on a funky hook!

Keep one basket or box for things you don't have time to tidy away, but clear it out once a week.

If all else fails, ban people from going in - or pay Mum to tidy behind you!

If you want to be really organised, arrange your books and music alphabetically. It's a bit of a bore to do, but then finding things is so easy!

Don't try to do everything at once or you'll get fed up and bored. Take a break with a pal or ask her to help!

Gorgeous Girl Do not Disturb

Did You Know?

Florence Nightingale carried a small owl in her pocket. Why? We've no idea!

Our fingernails grow faster than our toenails.

People who are genuphobic are afraid of knees.

A collection of ferrets is known as a business.

The longest recorded flight of a chicken is 13 seconds.

An ostrich's eye is bigger than its brain!

Donald Duck was banned in Finland because he didn't wear trousers. Oh-er!

If you're scared of being tickled by feathers, then you suffer from pteronophobia, Ha, ha, ha!

Bunty's Four Marys first appeared in 1958 – and they're still in the Third Form. They don't look a day older, either!

Superstition says that an acorn placed on a windowsill will keep lightning from coming in.

A fear of snow is known as chionophobia.

A collection of sardines is called a family. (We thought it was a can!)

Oh, I do like to be beside the seaside...

24

Tin openers were invented 48 years after tinned food.

Ketchup was first sold as medicine. Mmm! Nice!

All the food he could want — but nothing to open it with.

When walruses gather together, it's called a huddle!

More than one unicorn is called a blessing (or a miracle!).

Fear of going to school is called didaskaleinophobia.

Please don't make me go in! Please!

In Australia, water goes down the plughole in an anti-clockwise direction.

In some places it is considered unlucky to see a left handed person first thing on a Thursday morning.

Peladophobia is a fear of bald people!

Quick Quiz
How smart are you?

1. No piece of paper can be folded more than seven times. True or false

2. A fear of horses is known as
a) Rhinophobia
b) Hippophobia
c) Ponyphobia

3. Pack is the collective word for which of the following?
a) Cub scouts
b) Cards
c) Dogs

ANSWERS
1. True; 2. b); 3. All three.

A group of ducks on the water is called a paddling. In flight it's called a – er – flight.

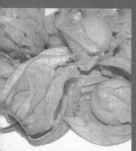

FRUIT PICKIN'

F	M	M	T	O	C	I	R	P	A	S	E	E	J	Z
S	T	A	R	F	R	U	I	T	T	y	n	g	n	s
H	Z	n	D	R	n	M	I	R	D	A	i	n	y	S
C	Z	D	Z	J	U	O	A	A	y	R	R	A	G	O
A	E	A	U	L	y	W	M	A	C	H	E	R	R	y
E	U	R	P	y	B	R	P	E	U	G	G	O	I	L
P	X	I	J	E	C	A	R	B	L	K	n	R	B	E
K	W	n	R	O	P	R	C	E	U	F	A	B	n	A
y	R	R	E	B	K	C	A	L	B	S	T	I	D	P
A	y	M	L	I	M	E	M	n	P	E	R	G	G	P
P	n	E	A	M	J	V	S	B	B	A	S	R	G	L
K	E	A	I	n	I	W	E	E	T	E	A	O	E	E
I	y	A	n	X	G	R	y	C	T	P	R	P	O	n
W	S	Z	R	A	R	O	E	P	E	P	K	R	K	G
I	F	O	R	y	B	n	O	L	E	M	X	V	y	W

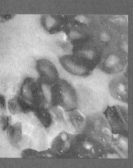

Get ready for some serious searching with our mega-fresh and fruity wordsearch. The words listed can read up, down, back, forwards or diagonally, and letters can be used more than once.

apple	gooseberry	mango	pear
apricot	grape	melon	plum
banana	kiwi	nectarine	raspberry
blackberry	lemon	orange	star fruit
cherry	lime	papaya	strawberry
cranberry	mandarin	peach	tangerine

Quiz Time!

Later –

So –

Then –

NOW, LET'S SEE HOW WE GET ON WITH THIS TV SHOW.

And –

WELL, WE GOT TEN ANSWERS. THAT'S NOT TOO BAD!

TRUE! BUT WE'LL HAVE TO DO EVEN BETTER IF WE WANT TO WIN THE QUIZ!

A few days later –

QUIZZES AND QUESTIONS! THAT'S ALL SHE EVER TALKS ABOUT, MUM! IT'S BORING!

NONSENSE! IT'S NO MORE BORING THAN WATCHING FOOTBALL, MIKE. ANYWAY, IT'S IMPORTANT. IF AMY WINS, SHE'LL BE REPRESENTING THE SCHOOL.

THE BIG QUIZ BOOK

And, in the first round of the quiz –

TOP MARKS, AMY AND HANNAH! WELL DONE!

COOL!

THE WAY WE'RE GOING, WE COULD MAYBE JUST WIN!

YEAH!

28

Later, at home —

Eventually —

29

So, at home –

Then the big day arrived –

But –

And –

Afterwards –

31

THE END

Spring, summer, autumn or winter! The time of year you were born can tell a lot about the things you like and the way you think. So read on...

Season's

Spring

Eyes down if you were born in March, April or May!

Friendly and outgoing, that's you! You like to be centre of any group and are well known for being the life and soul of the party.

Parties, shopping and meeting up with mates are among your favourite things.

Spring girlies are born leaders — but try not to be too bossy. It's important to stand back and let others take the lead at times!

While you like the fun of going around in a crowd in town, you like long walks in the country, too — especially in springtime.

You love fluffy, cuddly toys, and your favourite flowers are daffodils and tulips. Pick a bunch for good luck.

Wear yellow, pale green and cream for good luck — and steer clear of black or dark purple.

Your No1 food is chocolate — especially creamy eggs. Mmmm!

Autumn

Take a bow if you were born in September, October or November.

Autumn girls are kind and thoughtful. You'd help anyone in need!

One of your favourite sounds is the rustle of autumn leaves as they scatter below your feet. Just don't kick the pile Dad's just gathered, okay?

The best colours for autumn girlies are browns and golds. Don't worry if that sounds boring, cos blue and scarlet can bring good luck, too!

Although you tend to be a bit on the shy side with strangers, you can certainly sparkle when you're with your mates!

Reading is one of your top pastimes — and the one thing you don't like to lend is your fave books!

Nuts and crisps are your favourite nibbles. And you're likely to be a whizz at inventing groovy sandwich fillings!

For luck, wear an animal charm necklace or brooch.

Greetings!

Summer

Born in June, July or August? Then this could be you!

You love being busy — but don't like to be the organiser. You'll happily leave all the planning to others.

Like all summer girlies, you love lazing about in the warm summer sun. Give you a sun lounger and a cool drink, and you're happy as a king.

Your sunny nature means you're seldom without a friend or two around. And you'll have as many boy buddies as girl pals.

When it comes to food, you're a total fruit freak! And as for tutti-frutti ice cream — bliss!

Being a summer sizzler, you love hot colours like red, bright orange and pink — but not all together, please!

One of your favourite pastimes is gossiping! You know all the latest goss and just love passing it on to anyone who'll listen.

Extra good luck could be yours if you wear some shell jewellery.

Winter

December, January and February — now it's your turn!

Winter girlies will always stand out in the crowd! And your crowd is likely to be huge!

You can be a bit secretive and distant at times. You love your friends — but you don't mind being on your own from time to time.

At the first snowflake you're off to make a snowman — the biggest and best around. Bet you'd even make an igloo if you could!

You can be quite superstitious. If you have a lucky charm, you like to have it with you all the time!

When it comes to collections, you're the queen. If it's cheap and cheerful you'll collect it — for a while, anyway.

Colours which work best for winter girlies include silver, pink and pale blue.

Cooking (and eating) is something you love — along with art, music and crafts. You've too many hobbies to ever feel bored!

The Four Marys

THE FOUR MARYS, Simpy, Cotty, Raddy and Fieldy, were best friends in the Third Form at St Elmo's School for girls. It was nearing the end of the summer term and the girls were spending Sunday afternoon relaxing in their study —

GUESS WHAT! I'VE DONE IT! I'VE WON!

WON WHAT, FIELDY? A HOCKEY MATCH?

NO — WELL, YES — BUT THAT'S NOT WHAT'S EXCITING. I'VE WON THE DORIS SMYTHE SPORTS AWARD THIS YEAR. I'VE WON A WEEK'S HOLIDAY FOR ME AND A FRIEND.

WELL DONE. HAVE ALL THE WINNERS BEEN ANNOUNCED?

NO. BUT I HEARD MRS MITCHELL TELLING MISS GRAY WHEN I WAS IN THE CHANGING ROOMS. THE OFFICIAL ANNOUNCEMENT IS TOMORROW AT ASSEMBLY.

WELL, ONE THING IS SURE — I WON'T WIN ANYTHING. NOT UNLESS THERE'S A PRIZE FOR MOST MAGAZINES READ AND TV WATCHED IN A TERM.

BUT SIMPY MIGHT WIN THE OVERALL PRIZE. I MEAN, SHE'S DEAD CLEVER.

36

Raddy was, and soon —

I SEE MABEL'S CHANGED HER MIND ABOUT HATING SCOTLAND.

YEAH! SHE DIDN'T WANT TO COME WITH *ME*, BUT SHE JUMPED AT THE CHANCE WHEN CYNTHIA ASKED. HUH!

IT'S A PITY MISS CREEF HAS COME WITH US, THOUGH. IT WOULD HAVE BEEN MUCH MORE FUN WITH ONE OF THE YOUNGER TEACHERS.

STILL, IT BEATS SCHOOL. AND I CAN'T WAIT TO SEE THE PLACE WHERE WE'RE STAYING. IT'S SUPPOSED TO BE BEAUTIFUL!

A few hours later —

POOR VERONICA. SHE'S BEEN FEELING SICK EVER SINCE THE PLANE TOOK OFF — AND THIS BUS JOURNEY HAS JUST FINISHED HER OFF.

AND MABEL'S JUST THE SAME. THEY CAN'T HELP BEING ALIKE, THAT PAIR.

NEARLY THERE, GIRLS.

THIS IS RIDICULOUS! THE PLANE WAS *SO* CROWDED. I'M USED TO LUXURY JETS, YOU KNOW.

I WONDER WHAT WE'LL GET FOR TEA! I'M STARVING!

The thought was too much for Veronica —

STOP THE COACH! *PLEASE!* I'M GOING TO BE SICK!

ARGH! NOT ON ME!

MIND THE BOGS OUT THERE, MISS.

Eventually —

WELCOME TO LOCHAVERDALE HOUSE, GIRLS. I HOPE YOU HAD A PLEASANT JOURNEY.

HUH! HARDLY. AND I'M FREEZING!

ME — ME TOO. AND I-I'M ALL WET AND MUDDY FROM STEPPING IN A BOG!

POOR THINGS! I'LL PUT THEM TOGETHER IN THE GROUND FLOOR BEDROOM. THEY CAN HAVE A BATH AND GO STRAIGHT TO BED WHILE YOU OTHERS EAT. MY DAUGHTER WILL SHOW YOU THE WAY, MISS CREEF.

THANK YOU, LADY LOCHAVER.

LADY LOCHAVER! I THOUGHT SHE WAS A HOUSEKEEPER.

THIS IS THE DINING ROOM. ONCE YOU'VE TAKEN YOUR LUGGAGE UPSTAIRS, COME BACK HERE AND HELP YOURSELVES.

WOW! WHAT A SPREAD.

And —

THIS IS LOVELY. WHAT'S YOUR ROOM LIKE, COTTY?

THE SAME — AND THESE CONNECTING DOORS ARE GREAT. SARAH AND JAMILLA ARE ON THE OTHER SIDE.

ONLY MABEL AND VERONICA ARE DOWNSTAIRS — AND MISS CREEF OF COURSE.

YEAH! WONDER WHAT WE'LL BE DOING TOMORROW!

I WONDER IF WE'RE NEAR THE SEA!

They soon found out. Next morning —

OH, IT'S BEAUTIFUL! FIELDY, QUICK! TELL COTTY TO COME THROUGH AND LOOK AT THIS!

ISN'T IT GORGEOUS? LOOK AT THE SEALS BASKING ON THE ROCKS. AND THERE ARE BOATS WE CAN USE TO REACH THE ISLANDS.

COME ON. LET'S GET DRESSED AND EXPLORE THE BEACH BEFORE BREAKFAST.

OKAY! SEE YOU THERE!

HI! YOU TWO ARE UP EARLY. ISN'T IT BEAUTIFUL HERE?

YEAH! BUT DID YOU HEAR THE NOISE LAST NIGHT? THAT STRANGE CLANKING SOUND.

WE — WE HARDLY SLEPT. WE — WE THOUGHT IT WAS GHOSTS!

GHOSTS! HA, HA, HA! NO WAY! I HEARD IT, TOO, AND IT WAS THE PLUMBING. YOU OFTEN GET THESE NOISES IN OLD HOUSES.

PHEW! WE NEVER THOUGHT ABOUT THAT!

HA, HA, HA! THE PHANTOM OF THE PLUMBING SYSTEM. *WOOOOO!*

GIRLS! *GIRLS!*

WHAT IS IT, FIELDY? WHAT'S WRONG?

I — I SAW IT! I SAW A GHOST! *HONESTLY!*

WHAT? DON'T BE DAFT, FIELDY. YOU MUST HAVE BEEN SEEING THINGS.

NO, I WASN'T. I CAME OUT OF THE ROOM INTO THE CORRIDOR — AND THERE SHE WAS, DRESSED IN A MAID'S COSTUME.

SHE PROBABLY *WAS* A MAID! THEY MUST HAVE LOTS IN A HOUSE THIS BIG.

BUT IT WAS AN OLD-FASHIONED OUTFIT AND — AND AS I WATCHED, SHE DISAPPEARED RIGHT THROUGH THE WALL AT THE END OF THE CORRIDOR.

39

Continued on page 94

★ Perfect Pals!

Do be yourself

The best way to be a perfect pal is to be yourself. If you have to work at being a certain kind of friend, then the friendship isn't likely to last. Remember, you choose friends because you like them they way they are. Your friends choose you for the same reason.

Do trust her

Friendship is all about trust, and if that trust is broken, then a friendship can seldom survive. You've got to trust your buddy — and make sure she trusts you, too.

Do have fun

Friendship is all about having fun — so enjoy. Whether you're gossiping, shopping or giving each other make overs, have fun!

Don't worry

Don't get in a panic if you fall out now and again. All friends do, you know. As long as you can apologise if you hurt each other, then your friendship will last and last.

Don't be clingy

Don't be jealous if your friend has other mates besides you. It's actually much better if you both have lots of friends, because that way you're not so likely to become bored with each other.

Don't blab

If a friend tells you a secret, don't ever tell anyone else. Your friend will be really upset if she finds out (and she will find out!), so don't risk losing her friendship. It's not worth it!

There's more to being a mate than just hanging out together.
We give you some dos and don'ts on how to be the perfect pal!

Do be honest

If a friend asks for your opinion on something, then try to be as honest as you can — without offending her, of course. There are times to keep quiet, but what you mustn't do is tell her you think her new top's fine — then laugh about her when she's out of sight.

Do listen

If your friend has a problem — or just wants to talk about something — always be ready to listen, even if you don't think it's important.

Do share

Friends are great for sharing — not just clothes and books and stuff like that, but thoughts and secrets, too. A good friend is always ready to share.

Don't be two-faced

No matter how tempted you are, try not to talk about your friend to others. Someone is sure to tell her what you've been saying — and that'll mean trouble!

Don't be bossy

You may be best pals, but there will still be times you want to do different things. Accept this, and don't force your mate to always go along with your ideas.

Don't blame her

We all have days when we feel rough — but don't blame a friend if things aren't going well. And don't blame her for your bad mood, either. It's easy to take moods out on those we care about, so be careful!

IT was half past twelve on a sweltering night in August, and Selena's hair was driving her mad. The fringe kept flopping in her eyes and bits at the side were falling into her mouth. Selena had always loved her long, thick hair – but not now! Right at this moment she hated her hair more than she'd ever hated anything.

Selena got out of bed and tiptoed to her sister's room, where Evie was fast asleep and snoring. Next to her was a painting she had done in class. There were paints on

The Haircut

a table by her bed along with coloured paper, and, best of all, there was a pair of scissors. Selena shook her sister gently.

"Evie, could you do me a favour?"

Ten minutes later Selena's brown hair lay in clumps on the floor. She felt so much cooler.

As she looked at herself in the mirror, she could see that her hair looked a bit strange. It was spiky and lop-sided. The fringe covered most of her left eye and was inches above her right one, but at least she could see and breathe a bit better.

★ ★ ★ ★

"Not bad, Evie," she said. "You'll make a hairdresser yet."

"What d'you think Mum'll say?" Evie asked.

Selena came down to earth with a bump. Her mother was so proud of Selena's hair. Every time she brushed it, she said how beautiful it was.

"Oh, we'll get round Mum," said Selena confidently. "She lets us choose our own clothes, so why shouldn't we choose our own hairstyles?"

"I don't suppose it'll make any difference in the audition," said Evie casually.

Selena gasped. The audition! How on earth had she forgotten? She had been growing her hair to get the part in the pantomime everyone wanted — the part of Cinderella.

Selena and Evie went to drama classes on Saturdays. The highlight of term was the school pantomime, and this term a professional director was coming to choose the actors.

"Evie," she shouted. "Look what you've done to my hair! I don't stand a chance of getting a part now."

"But you asked me to do it!" said Evie. "It was your idea!"

"I just asked you to cut the fringe," said Selena, "not make a terrible mess like this."

"Why don't you wear one of Mum's hats at the audition?" suggested Evie.

"Cinderella wouldn't wear a hat! She's a scullery maid, who cleans up cinders," snapped Selina.

"How about a scarf, then? That might look good."

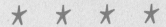

It was the day of the audition, and Selena joined the queue of girls. There was Candy, with her beautiful long blonde hair — a perfect romantic Cinderella. And Masumi, with loads of shiny black locks. Selena could have cried. She was wearing a black and white scarf with tassels on it, and she knew she looked awful.

Then a voice called out, "Miss Selena Martin."

Selena was so nervous that she tripped as she walked on to the stage and the scarf fell off, revealing her horrible hair to the world.

She was about to give up and go home, when she heard the director whisper to his assistant.

"That's her! That's the girl! I'm sick of girlie Cinderellas. I want a girl with spirit — a punk princess!"

"Maybe," thought Selena, as she picked up the script, "maybe this haircut wasn't such a bad idea after all."

The End

Summer

45

47

. . . SO I'VE TO HAVE TOTAL REST FOR AT LEAST A WEEK.

POOR YOU!

IT'S NOT EVEN AS IF YOU'LL MISS ANY SCHOOL, WITH IT BEING THE HOLIDAYS.

BUT AT LEAST YOU'LL BE ABLE TO DO ALL THE READING AND TV VIEWING THAT YOU WANT.

SO I WILL. HEY, MAYBE THIS WASN'T SO BAD AFTER ALL.

WE'LL LEAVE YOU TO IT, THEN.

THANKS FOR COMING!

Next day —

RIGHT THEN! WHERE'LL I START?

And —

THIS IS THE LIFE! I'VE JUST WATCHED A WHOLE FILM AND TWO EPISODES OF FRIENDS!

A little later —

HOW ARE YOU DOING?

FINE, MUM. I'VE READ AND WATCHED LOADS.

That evening —

MMM. I DUNNO IF I CAN GO ANOTHER EPISODE OF FRIENDS.

AND THESE MAGAZINES ARE ALL THE SAME. BO-ORING!

Just then the phone rang —

HOW ARE YOU GETTING ON THEN? 'BET YOU'VE HAD A FANTASTIC TIME!

WELL . . .

. . . ACTUALLY, I'M BORED! PLEASE COME ROUND!

NO PROBLEM, LOUISE!

IT WAS NICE TO CATCH UP ON SOME VIDEOS AND STUFF, BUT NOTHING'S MORE IMPORTANT THAN HAVING TIME OUT WITH MY MATES!

THE END

49

GLITTERAMA!

**Want to hold the perfect glitter party?
We asked Amy, Danielle and Zara to show you how!**

Danielle loves this glittery purple top and sparkly jeans.

Zara's sparkly dress doubles as a top with glittery trousers!

Amy wears a sparkly top, trousers with a sparkly belt and a silver hairband. Wow!

fab party fun

* go crazy and wrap tinsel everywhere - even although it's not Christmas

* spray balloons and streamers with glitter

* eat fairy cakes decorated with hundreds and thousands or metallic balls

* ask if you can use indoor sparklers

* for extra sparkle, dip your nails in glitter before your nail varnish is dry!

* use silver or gold coloured plates and cups!

Danielle thinks these wings are 'fairy' good fun!

Amy stuck on these false nails then added glitter stickers!

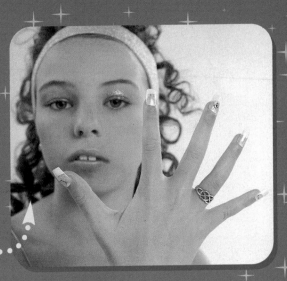

Zara shows off a butterfly 'tattoo' on her shoulder! (Just press it on and it'll peel off later.)

Amy's chosen a sparkly silver hairband.

Zara's a perfect princess in her tiara!

Danielle has sparkles at her eyes and glittery cheeks!

Amy loves her shimmery silver eyeshadow!

Now turn the page to find out how to make the perfect glitter party invitations!

PARTY TIME!

Amaze your mates with these wild party invitations!

Draw a star on card with glue then sprinkle star shapes or glitter over the top!

Blow up a balloon and write a funky party message on it with a marker pen. Write the details (time, place, day) on the reverse. When the balloon's deflated you'll find that the writing has a cool embossed effect!

Cut out a star and stick it to card with other smaller stars - cute!

Buy some glittery hair clasps and use them to attach your invite to a piece of card.

Stick one or two balloons to a card. Easy!

Make your invitations star-shaped in lots of cool colours.

Two stars in contrasting colours look fab stuck together!

You can also...

Put your invite inside a balloon and add some glitter. When the balloon's burst, the glitter and invite will float to the ground.

Whatever your invitations look like, fill their envelopes with glitter to give your friends a surprise when they open them!

Continued from page 19

The Comp

TYPICAL! ONLY JAYNE THE PAIN WOULD WALK OUT BECAUSE SHE BROKE A NAIL. SHE'S RUINED EVERYTHING!

REDVALE COMP was holding a Big Brother style game to raise money for charity. But Jayne the Pain had walked out after just one morning.

NO SHE HASN'T, BECKY. I BET THE PEOPLE WATCHING THINK IT'S GREAT!

Roz was right. In a room not far away —

50p FOR 30 MINUTES VIEWING

THIS IS BRILLIANT. BUT I WISH I COULD TELL BECKY NOT TO WORRY. IT'S ALL GOING GREAT.

YEAH! WATCHING GAVIN GREEN COOK SPUDS WAS COOL! BET HE'S NEVER SO MUCH AS BOILED AN EGG BEFORE.

MY MUM SAYS THIS KIND OF THING IS DEGRADING. IT ONLY APPEALS TO PEOPLE WITH A LOW INTELLIGENCE.

OH, YEAH? SO WHY DID YOU SPEND MONEY TO COME IN HERE AND WATCH WITH THE REST OF US, MARGARET?

WELL SAID, FREDDY.

OH — ER — I WAS JUST PASSING. AND — AND IT'S FOR CHARITY. I'M NOT STAYING.

HA, HA, HA!

HA, HA, HA!

53

Meanwhile —

RIGHT, BOYS, YOU WASH. THE GIRLS DRY AND PUT AWAY.

I'M *NOT* WEARING GLOVES AND AN APRON.

OKAY, *I'LL* DO IT.

But —

OI, WATCH IT, BOZO! I'M SOAKED NOW.

SHOULD HAVE WORN THE PINNY, GAVIN!

WHO DO YOU THINK WILL BE FIRST TO BE EVICTED, ROZ?

DUNNO. REMEMBER, THEY'VE DECIDED IT'S THE PERSON WITH *LEAST* VOTES WHO GETS KICKED OUT. JAYNE WOULDN'T HAVE GOT MANY — BUT SHE'S GONE. I THINK GAVIN WILL DO WELL, THOUGH . . .

YOU THINK SO? *WE* GET TO NOMINATE WHO THE PUBLIC VOTES FOR, REMEMBER, SO YOU GIRLS ARE ONE DOWN ALREADY!

HE'S RIGHT. THERE ARE THREE BOYS AND THEY MIGHT STICK TOGETHER.

YOU'RE RIGHT THERE, ROZ. I'M ALREADY PLANNING MY CELEBRATION PARTY!

I *WAS* GOING TO SAY, 'EVEN ALTHOUGH HE'S A BIG-HEADED RAT'! SO DON'T COUNT ON IT, BOY. I THINK *ANY* OF US COULD WIN.

NAH. HODGE DOESN'T LIKE GAVIN, AND STUART SEEMS QUITE A NICE GUY. THEY'LL NOMINATE WHO THEY WANT, NOT DO WHAT GAVIN TELLS THEM.

The next day —

RIGHT, YOUR TASK FOR THE WEEK WILL BE TO ACT AS A TEAM TO SEW THE PIECES OF MATERIAL INTO A PATCHWORK QUILT.

I CAN'T *WAIT* TO SEE GAVIN SEWING!

BUT, WHEN I BLOW THE WHISTLE, YOU WILL ALL STOP WHAT YOU'RE DOING AND START CLEANING THE TILED WALLS. OKAY?

OKAY, MISS BLISS. NO PROBLEMS.

CREEP.

NEED ANY HELP THREADING THE NEEDLE, GAVIN?

NAH. JUST WATCH THIS.

OUCH! I DO. THIS NEEDLE'S EYE IS TOO SMALL.

I'M ALL KNOTTED UP.

TRY A SHORTER THREAD LIKE ME.

HAH! LOOK AT HODGE SEWING! WHAT A WUSS!

SHUDDUP, FREDDY. YOU SHOULD BE SUPPORTING HODGE. I THOUGHT YOU WERE SUPPOSED TO BE HIS MATE!

OOOH, GET YOU! ALWAYS KNEW YOU HAD A FANCY FOR OLD HODGE, BRADY!

IGNORE HIM, LAURA. HE'S JUST TRYING TO WIND YOU UP.

I KNOW. I JUST SAW RED WHEN HE BADMOUTHED THE GAME.

WHAT'S WITH YOU TRADING INSULTS WITH FREDDY, LAURA?

OH, NOTHING. I JUST GOT ANNOYED WITH HIM BADMOUTHING THE GAME. I FELT HE SHOULD BE SUPPORTING HODGE, NOT MAKING FUN OF HIM.

MIND YOU, I WOULDN'T MIND GETTING TO KNOW JOE BETTER. HE'S KINDA CUTE.

WHAT? I THINK STEVE'S MUCH NICER. IN FACT, HE'S QUITE TASTY.

WELL, YOU CAN HAVE HIM. I'LL HAVE JOE, AND LAURA AND BECKY CAN SHARE HODGE AND FREDDY!

WOW! THANKS A LOT! I THINK I'LL PASS ON THAT, THANK YOU.

The following morning —

THE VOTES HAVE ALL BEEN COUNTED AND ROZ CUMMINGS HAS BEEN EVICTED FROM THE GAME.

OH, NO!

BAD LUCK, ROZ. BECKY'S ON HER OWN NOW!

YEAH — BUT SHE'LL BE OKAY. I JUST WISH THE GUYS WEREN'T SO PLEASED WITH THEMSELVES.

HAPPY NOW, ARE YOU? YOU'VE GOT RID OF ANOTHER GIRL?

ABSOLUTELY! SOON IT'LL BE JUST YOU AND ME LEFT. WON'T THAT BE NICE?

WHAT'S GOIN' ON? WHAT ON EARTH IS GAVIN UP TO NOW?

Continued on page 77

You Say...

We met up with six groovy girlies from Newcastle and asked them some very important questions.

If you could have anything in the world, what would you choose?

Basma

Basma A never-ending wardrobe packed with fashionable clothes.

Aia Endless money so I could buy whatever I wanted.

Hannah I'd like Dannii Minogue as my sister.

Penny My own huge shopping centre.

Paula Everlasting money.

Rachael Big feathery wings would be fabby.

Hannah

What couldn't you live without?

Hannah Chewing gum, a best friend and a toilet.
Penny My teddy!
Paula My blanket and my inhaler!
Rachael My glasses. I can't see a thing without them.
Basma Books and sweets!
Aia Chocolate and my glasses.

Rachael

If you could change your name, what would you choose?

Paula Katie.
Basma Basma – I like my name as it is.
Penny Amy.
Aia I don't think I'd want to change my name.
Hannah Richeal Mirissa.
Rachael Emma. And I'd choose a surname beginning with a, so I'd be first for everything.

What's your favourite sandwich filling?

Hannah Tuna and sweetcorn.
Rachael Peanut butter and jam.
Penny Chocolate spread.
Paula Crisps!
Basma Chocolate spread.
Aia Cheese.

Aia

What's your favourite way to spend a weekend?

Basma Going to the cinema without an adult.
Paula At home, watching TV with my friends.
Hannah Going shopping with a crowd of mates.
Aia At the beach with friends.
Penny Hanging out with my mates.
Rachael At a huge sleepover with loadsa sweets and no bedtime!

Paula

What's your favourite TV programme?

Aia Anything. I like lots of programmes.
Penny The Simpsons and Coronation Street!
Rachael Friends.
Paula Friends, The Simpsons and Sabrina.
Hannah Big Brother, The Simpsons and EastEnders.
Basma Everything!

Penny

Favourite Football team?

All NEWCASTLE UNITED! 'Way the Magpies!

Did You Know?

More funky facts to make you smile!

If you are scared of spiders, then you are arachnophobic.

Coca-Cola was originally green. Blee!

More than half London's 'underground' is above ground!

In Florida it is illegal to sing while wearing a swimsuit!

It may seem weird, but it is thought to be lucky if a bird – er – poos on you!

Fear of kissing is called philemaphobia!

Er – it's not that I don't like you, Cecil. I–I'm just philemaphobic! Honestly!

Jellyfish can sting, even after they're dead.

4,000 FOOT DROP!

Kangaroos can't walk backwards.

If the colour red makes you quake, then you may be suffering from erythrophobia. In that case we'd suggest you don't wear it!

Some people believe it is unlucky to point at the moon!

Oh, boy! What do I do now?

Frogs have teeth, but toads don't.

If you're surrounded by a group of tigers, it's called an ambush – honestly

Quick Quiz

Test your knowledge here.

1. Superstition says that if you wash your face in the morning dew on the 1st of May, you will be...
a) Rich for a year?
b) Beautiful for a year?
c) Wet for a year?

2. A collection of hippopotamuses is known as a blubber. True or false?

3. A fear of dancing is...
a) Stepophobia?
b) Discophobia?
c) Chorophobia?

ANSWERS
1. b); 2. False, it's a bloat; 3. c)

Lots of leopards is known as a leap!

Donkeys kill more people than plane crashes.

A group of crows is called a murder. Call on Columbo Crow!

Hot water weighs more than cold.

Samhainophobia is a fear of Hallowe'en. Aaaaaaargh!

If you spot a group of caterpillars or ants on the move, it is called an army.

A group of cats is a clowder.

At the double! Qui-ick march!

A fear of washing is known as abultophobia. Lots of little boys seem to suffer from this.

Cross Eyed!

These items have all been photographed from unusual angles. Look closely and see if you can spot what they are.

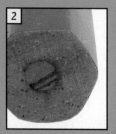

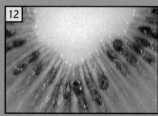

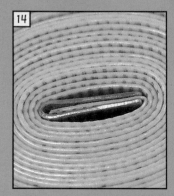

Answers

1.Spiral notebook; 2.Pencil;
3.Pencil sharpener; 4.Battery;
5.Thread; 6.Pen; 7.Make-up brush;
8.Hair brush; 9.Roll of film;
10.Picture frame; 11.Corkscrew;
12.Kiwi fruit; 13.Screwdriver;
14.Tape measure; 15.CD.

NOW I'LL RING FOR BROWN.

BROWN! THE FIRE HAS GONE OUT AGAIN. SEE TO IT IMMEDIATELY.

YES, LADY LUCINDA.

THERE'S SOMETHING ODD HERE. THE FIRE WAS FINE A FEW MINUTES AGO.

THESE COALS ARE DAMP, AND THE WATER JUG'S EMPTY. LADY LUCINDA MUST HAVE PUT IT OUT ON PURPOSE. TCH! WHAT A SPITEFUL THING TO DO.

NOW DRAW THE SHADES FOR ME. I'M GOING TO HAVE A LIE DOWN. IT'S VERY TIRING BEING A LADY.

NOT HALF AS TIRING AS BEING A MAID, I'LL BET!

Lady Lucinda dozed off. Then, a little later —

OH, GOOD! IT SOUNDS AS IF WE HAVE A VISITOR.

DOCTOR ROPER — THIS IS A PLEASANT SURPRISE! BUT WHAT BRINGS YOU HERE? WE ARE ALL QUITE WELL.

I'M PLEASED TO HEAR IT, LADY RICE. BUT I WANTED TO HAVE A TALK WITH YOU — ABOUT LADY LUCINDA.

THEY'VE SHUT THE DOOR, BUT I CAN HEAR WHAT THEY'RE SAYING ABOUT ME FROM OUT HERE.

DO YOU REMEMBER THE NURSE WHO ATTENDED YOU WHEN LUCINDA WAS BORN? A MRS WICKEN FROM THE VILLAGE.

YES, I REMEMBER HER, DOCTOR.

MRS WICKEN HAS RECENTLY DIED, AND ON HER DEATH-BED SHE MADE A CONFESSION TO ME. IT SEEMS THAT AT THE TIME YOU HAD LUCINDA, MRS WICKEN'S SISTER WAS ALSO DELIVERED OF A DAUGHTER, A GIRL CALLED EMMA BROWN.

THAT'S EMMA — OUR MAID.

"That is correct. She was a sickly babe."

POOR MITE! THIS ONE NEEDS EXTRA WARMTH AND NOURISHMENT OR SHE'LL SURELY DIE.

BUT WHERE WILL SHE GET THAT HERE? OUR COTTAGE IS COLD AND DAMP, AND THERE'S SCARCE ENOUGH FOOD FOR US ALL AS IT IS. MY BABY IS DOOMED!

MAYBE NOT. MY MISTRESS, LADY JANE, HAS JUST HAD A HEALTHY DAUGHTER. I'LL SWOP THE BABIES OVER FOR A WHILE! LADY JANE'S CHILD WILL NOT DIE HERE, AND YOUR SICKLY BABE WILL BE WELL LOOKED AFTER AT THE BIG HOUSE.

MRS WICKEN TOLD ME THAT WHEN SHE SWAPPED THE BABIES YOU WERE TOO ILL TO NOTICE. BUT LATER, WHEN THE SICKLY CHILD HAD GROWN WELL AND STRONG, THERE WAS NO CHANCE TO SWOP THEM BACK.

YOU — YOU MEAN THE SERVANT, EMMA, IS REALLY MY DAUGHTER, AND THE GIRL I'VE CHERISHED ALL THESE YEARS IS A PAUPER'S CHILD?

66

LOOK AT MY HAIR! IT'S COME LOOSE ALREADY! WHAT A CARELESS CREATURE YOU ARE. YOU'D BETTER START ALL OVER AGAIN!

SHE DID THAT ON PURPOSE! JUST LIKE I USED TO. SHE'S GETTING HER OWN BACK.

By tea-time —

I CAN'T GO ON. I'M EXHAUSTED. I MUST CLOSE MY EYES FOR A SECOND . . .

LUCY! WAKE UP . . .

. . . WAKE UP! WAKE UP!

I-I'M SORRY! I FELL ASLEEP. OH! WHERE AM I?

IN YOUR BEDROOM OF COURSE, MY DARLING. YOU'VE HAD A LITTLE NAP. TIME TO GET UP FOR TEA NOW.

IT — IT WAS ALL JUST A DREAM! OH, THANK GOODNESS! I AM STILL LADY LUCINDA, AND EMMA IS THE MAID.

YOU RANG, MY LADY?

YES. FETCH MY SHOES, EMMA. THEY'RE OVER THERE.

Charlie
BUSTED

IT'S A WRAP!

The shops are shut and you've a pressie to wrap! Help!

Here's how to use things you might already have at home to get all wrapped up!

read all about it!

Wrap your present in newspaper, tie with twine then shred the extra paper at the top into a 'rosette'. Make a label by cutting out a piece of white paper then sticking the name of the person you're giving your gift to on a piece of brown paper. Glue this on to the white panel before sticking it to your gift - easy!

paper power!

Cut out letters from newspapers and stick them to brown paper. Spell out the name of the person who's receiving your gift or use letters randomly. Make a matching gift tag by sticking letters to another piece of paper, stuck on to card. Punch a hole in it - then tie it on with string.

fab flags!

Make flags by sticking triangles of bright cellophane (sweet wrappers are ideal) to string. Wrap the string around your present, then use the same paper with pieces of the same colour of cellophane to make a tag.

aw! sweet!

Cut cellophane strips from sweet wrappers and stick them randomly on to any bright paper you have. Do the same with your tag.

clever cardboard!

To wrap a flat square present, cut pieces of cardboard which are the same width and length as the gift. Then wrap them around it widthways and lengthways, before tying it with a piece of netting from fruit or vegetables.

round and round!

Cut circles from foil sweet wrappers and stick them to plain white paper. Easy!

bubble trouble!

Wrap your present in coloured tissue, then in bubble wrap. A matching tag can be made by sticking the same tissue paper to card then topping with a sliver of bubble wrap.

orange and lemon!

Wrap your gift in tissue paper and then wrap the netting from a bag of oranges around it - easy!

ready ribbon!

Jazz up white paper with 'ribbon' made by cutting carrier bags into strips - the brighter, the better! Stick an extra piece on to card if you want to make a tag.

colour code!

Paint string any colour you like and use it to tie your present. Draw or print a pretty design to match or contrast on your paper - brown or coloured!

Are You A Crimbo Cracker?

Find out
with our fun
flowchart.

START

Do you prefer tinsel to holly?

no

yes

Would you choose a real Christmas tree?

Do you own lots of glittery make-up?

yes

no

no

Is Santa always left a 'snack' in your house?

yes

Do you hate going to the shops at Christmas?

no

Is there a fairy at the top of your Christmas tree?

no

yes

yes

yes

Is money better than a present?

no

Do you like singing or listening to Christmas songs?

Are you really happy if it snows at Christmas?

no

Do you love going to Christmas parties?

yes

yes

no

yes

yes

Christmas? You just want it to be over. You can't wait for the warm summer days to come round again, cos that's the time you have most fun.

You love Christmas - especially if it's an old-fashioned family affair. Lots of pressies, food and games in front of a cosy fire make you a happy girlie.

You like Christmas to sizzle with parties and glitter. Wow! And as for snow, well, it's okay - as long as it doesn't stop you getting out to all your parties.

WHAT'S WITH YOU AND FREDDY AGAIN, LAURA? I KNOW HE'S A PAIN, BUT YOU SHOULD JUST IGNORE HIM.

I KNOW, BUT I JUST FEEL HE SHOULD BE SUPPORTING HODGE, NOT GAVIN. SOMETIMES I THINK *YOU* LOT ARE SUPPORTING GAVIN, TOO.

GET REAL, LAURA. THERE'S NO WAY WE WANT GAVIN TO WIN! WE'RE JUST HAVING A LAUGH WITH THE LADS.

HUH! IF YOU SAY SO.

I'M NOT CONVINCED. MAYBE THEY THINK STEVE AND JOE'LL BE IMPRESSED IF THEY BACK THEIR MATE.

Meanwhile, in the block —

ER — GOT A MINUTE, BECKY? I NEED SOME HELP HERE. WHAT DO I DO NEXT?

NOTHING, HODGE — NOT IF YOU WANT THAT PASTRY TO BE EDIBLE. I'LL BE OVER IN A MINUTE.

And —

SHAKE SOME FLOUR ONTO THE TABLE — BUT NOT TOO HARD! *AAARGH!*

WOOPS! TOO LATE. SORRY.

HA, HA, HA! YOU SHOULD SEE YOURSELVES. HERE, HODGE. WIPE SOME OFF WITH THIS CLOTH.

LET ME HELP YOU, BECKY. IT CERTAINLY SEEMS TO BE MY MORNING FOR AIDING THE LADY IN DISTRESS.

GIVE IT A REST, GAVIN. YOU'RE JUST TRYING TO MAKE YOURSELF LOOK GOOD. I'LL CLEAN MYSELF, THANK YOU.

OKAY, YOU LOT. ENOUGH HILARITY. GET THIS MESS SEEN TO AT THE DOUBLE. AFTER LUNCH WE'LL BE HAVING TODAY'S NOMINATIONS.

AND I KNOW WHO *I'M* GONNA NOMINATE.

Soon —

...SO I THINK IT SHOULD BE GAVIN WHO'S ELIMINATED NEXT. MY REASON? EM — HE'S A TOTAL PAIN. WILL THAT DO?

But —

WELL, THAT MEANS IT'S HODGE AND GAVIN WHO ARE UP FOR EVICTION TOMORROW. IT'LL BE GAV WHO GETS MY VOTE TO STAY.

MINE TOO, STEVE.

AND MINE.

I DON'T BELIEVE IT! YOU'LL VOTE FOR THAT CREEP RATHER THAN YOUR FRIEND, FREDDY? AND AS FOR *YOU*, HAYLEY, WHY CAN'T YOU SUPPORT YOUR SISTER? YOU SHOULD WANT TO HELP HER GET RID OF THE PAIN.

THAT'S ENOUGH, LAURA. IF YOU CAN'T BEHAVE, YOU WILL HAVE TO LEAVE THE ROOM.

SORRY, MISS.

THEY MAKE ME *SOOO* MAD.

At break —

DON'T GET SO UPSET ABOUT EVERYTHING, LAURA. I'LL VOTE FOR HODGE TO STAY IF YOU REALLY WANT.

OH, IT DOESN'T MATTER, HAYLEY. I JUST GET SO MAD AT FREDDY. I'D HATE IT IF *MY* FRIENDS DIDN'T SUPPORT *ME!*

But not everyone wanted Hodge to stay —

STAND BACK, EVERYONE. I'LL SOON HAVE THIS UNDER CONTROL — WHICH IS MORE THAN I CAN SAY FOR *YOU*, HODGSON. IF *I* HAD A VOTE YOU'D BE OUT *NOW!*

SORRY, SIR. I DIDN'T REALISE THE COOKER WAS STILL ON WHEN I PUT THE CLOTH ON TOP.

HA, HA, HA! TRUST HODGE. WHAT A DIVVY!

GAV'S SURE TO WIN THE VOTE NOW — I HOPE!

THERE YOU GO AGAIN, FREDDY. ALL YOU EVER DO IS SUPPORT GAVIN AND BAD-MOUTH HODGE. YOU'RE A DISLOYAL PIG!

OOOH, TOUCHY AREN'T WE? I'M ONLY HAVING A LAUGH.

WELL IT'S NOT FUNNY — SO GIVE IT A BREAK OR I . . .

THAT'LL DO, LAURA. I'VE HAD ENOUGH OF YOU TWO ARGUING. LEAVE THE ROOM — *BOTH* OF YOU!

BUT I'VE GOT TWENTY-FIVE MINUTES LEFT BEFORE MY MONEY'S UP.

TOO BAD, FREDERICKS. ANY MORE LIP AND YOU'LL BE BANNED FOR GOOD.

OOOPS! I FEEL BAD ABOUT THIS. BUT TRUST THE BLIZZARD TO BE ON DUTY.

LOOK, I-I'M SORRY FOR GETTING YOU THROWN OUT, FREDDY. BUT I JUST GOT SO MAD AT YOU SUPPORTING GAVIN INSTEAD OF HODGE.

I'M NOT REALLY SUPPORTING THE BIG-HEAD, YOU KNOW. I WAS JUST BAITING YOU. SO I SUPPOSE I DESERVED TO GET INTO TROUBLE.

ACTUALLY, I'M MISSING HODGE. STEVE AND JOE AREN'T AS MUCH FUN TO GO AROUND WITH. AND AFTER SCHOOL HE'S TOO TIRED TO GO ANYWHERE.

AH, THAT JUST PROVES HOW HARD IT IS IN DOMESTIC CLASS. BUT SERIOUSLY, LET'S CALL A TRUCE. OKAY?

OKAY! NO MORE SNIPING OR STUPID COMMENTS. AND I PROMISE I'LL VOTE FOR HODGE — EVEN ALTHOUGH I'D RATHER HE WAS WATCHING WITH ME.

NOW THAT'S *TRUE* FRIENDSHIP.

GOOD FOR FREDDY. HE'S NOT SUCH A RAT, AFTER ALL.

Later —

. . . YOU SHOULD HAVE SEEN LAURA'S FACE, BECKY. I THOUGHT SHE WAS GONNA STRANGLE FREDDY.

REALLY?

YEAH! BUT WE'RE PALS NOW — WELL SORT OF.

BUT WHAT'S *THAT* ALL ABOUT? HAYLEY AND ROZ SEEM *VERY* CHUMMY WITH STEVE AND JOE. AM I MISSING SOMETHING?

WELL — ER — I DUNNO. ROZ AND HAYLEY ARE JUST CHATTING TO THE LADS, I THINK.

I DON'T THINK I WANT TO BE THE ONE TO TELL BECKY THAT HER SISTER IS KEEN ON STEVE.

WELL I JUST HOPE THEY'RE NICER THAN THEIR BIG-HEADED PAL. THE SOONER HE LEAVES THE GAME THE BETTER.

OH — ER — THEY'RE OKAY, BECKY.

AND THERE'S NO POINT IN TELLING HER THAT HAYLEY VOTED FOR GAVIN TO *STAY*, EITHER.

Later, as Laura watched TV —

I'LL GET THE DOOR. IT'S MAYBE BECKS.

But it was Freddy —

SORRY TO CALL ROUND LIKE THIS, BUT I WANTED TO GIVE YOU THESE. AND — ER — TO ASK IF YOU'D LIKE TO COME TO THE CINEMA ONE NIGHT.

FREDDY? OH, BUT I . . .

ERK! HOW DO I GET OUT OF *THIS*?

81

Continued on page 116

Makeover Magic!

FAB NEW LOOKS FOR AMY!

on your marks!

For Amy's first look she chose a sporty top and trousers trimmed with purple, her favourite colour, and teamed it with a white t-shirt. It's a perfect outfit for all kinds of activities - lounging around the house, going for a walk or actually being sporty! To go with this cool casual look, we put Amy's lovely long hair in a high ponytail then pleated it for a funky no-fuss style.

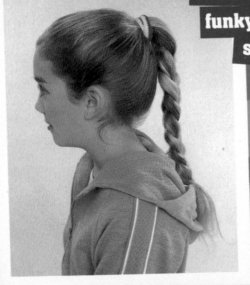

WHICH LOOK DID AMY LIKE BEST? *"I love the multi-coloured top and pink cords!"*

WAS THERE ANYTHING AMY DIDN'T LIKE? *"Yeah! My hair looks like it's in big rollers in my 'glam' look."*

groovy!

This cosy multi-coloured top was Amy's second choice and can be worn with almost any colour! Here she's matched it with dusky pink cords and soft beige boots. Amy decided this would be the perfect look for going shopping or meeting mates in a cafe - especially with her hair pulled up and braided into two French pleats.

ooh, wow!

Amy's final choice was a floaty pink top. For this, Amy was given a matching glam hairstyle, with her hair up on top of her head in a mass of curls. These were secured with a soft sparkly bauble which matched her top, turning her into a party princess!

For Maria's new looks, turn to pages 100 and 101.

Did You Know?

Even more funky facts to make you smile!

A bunch of bats is called a cloud.

Two or more hedgehogs is a prickle.

The word for a fear of everything is panophobia.

The Lake of Menteith is the only lake in Scotland. All the others are lochs.

In 1939 a shower of frogs fell in Towbridge!

Queen Elizabeth 1 had more than eighty wigs!

Central Park in New York is bigger than all of Monaco

A sneeze can travel at 100 miles an hour. Phew!

I'm what's known as the big-wig around here!

A fear of vegetables is achanophobia.

Let's see how you like being munched!

The first lamb you see in spring is said to bring good luck - but only if it's facing away from you, and isn't black!

Musophobia is a fear of mice.

If you're scared of ghosts, then you are phasmophobic. Boo!

In parts of India it is illegal to stick chewing gum to your nose. Mind you, we don't know why anyone would want to!

Fear of thinking is called phronemophobia!

Come on, scaredy cat!

In Wales it is considered unlucky to hear a cuckoo call before April 6.

Lots of giraffes is called a tower.

Penguins can jump up to six feet high.

HEIGHT 6 FT. 5'

Quick Quiz

It's testing time!

1. Which is the odd one out?
a) The King of Clubs
b) The King of Hearts
c) The King of Clubs
d) The King of Diamonds

2. True or false, Walt Disney suffered from musophobia?

3. Which colour should not be waved in front of a bull?
c) blue
d) green
e) red

A clutter is the collective noun for a group of spiders. Erk!

A gathering of owls is known as a parliament.

ANSWERS

1. b) The King of Hearts is the only one without a moustache; 2. True. Walt was scared of mice (but not Mickey, obviously); 3. All of them. Bulls are colour blind, so don't wave anything in front of them.

Autumn

HOLLY RICHARDSON and her friends were looking forward to the summer holidays —

I'M GOING TO GREECE AGAIN THIS YEAR.

WE'RE GOING TO FRANCE. HOW ABOUT *YOU*, HOLLY?

ME? OH, I'M GOING TO SPAIN!

SPAIN! ARE YOU REALLY?

BET THEY THOUGHT I'D SAY BLACKPOOL AGAIN, BUT NOT THIS YEAR. SPAIN FOR TWO WHOLE WEEKS — I CAN'T WAIT!

"It's Not Fair!"

At home —

HOLLY — I'VE GOT SOME EXCITING NEWS!

MAYBE DAD'S GOT AN EXTRA HOLIDAY, AND WE'RE GOING FOR *THREE* WEEKS!

YOUR SISTER, KATE, AND HER BOYFRIEND, JACK, ARE GETTING MARRIED — AND THEY WANT YOU TO BE BRIDESMAID!

THAT'S GREAT, MUM! WHEN'S THE WEDDING?

I KNOW! I'LL GET REALLY FAT SO THE DRESS WON'T FIT. THEN I *CAN'T* BE A BRIDESMAID!

So —

MORE PUDDING, HOLLY? BUT YOU'VE HAD TWO HELPINGS OF EVERYTHING ALREADY!

I KNOW, BUT I HAVEN'T GOT LONG TO GET FAT. I MUST EAT AS MUCH AS I CAN!

But, later —

OOOH! I FEEL SICK AND MY TUMMY HURTS! I'LL HAVE TO THINK OF SOMETHING ELSE.

The wedding drew nearer —

MUM, I'VE GOT A VERY IMPORTANT NETBALL MATCH A WEEK ON SATURDAY . . .

THAT'S KATE'S WEDDING DAY! YOU'LL JUST HAVE TO TELL THE TEAM YOU CAN'T MAKE IT.

BUT I *HAVE* TO BE THERE! I'M THEIR TOP SCORER!

AND *I* SAY YOU HAVE TO BE AT YOUR SISTER'S WEDDING! WHAT'S WRONG, HOLLY? MOST GIRLS WOULD *LOVE* TO BE A BRIDESMAID!

90

But, that night —

KATE LOOKED UPSET THIS MORNING. I DIDN'T MEAN TO HURT HER. I GUESS MUM'S RIGHT. I'VE BEEN A REAL PAIN!

So, next morning —

KATE, I'VE BROUGHT YOU THE MAIL AND YOUR BREAKFAST IN BED. IT'S TO SAY SORRY FOR THE WAY I'VE BEEN BEHAVING.

OH, HOLLY. I'M SORRY, TOO — ABOUT YOUR HOLIDAY . . .

IT DOESN'T MATTER. WE'LL GO ANOTHER YEAR, AND I DO WANT TO BE YOUR BRIDESMAID.

I'M SO GLAD, HOLLY. NOW WHO CAN THIS LETTER BE FROM?

Minutes later —

MUM! DAD! CANCEL THE CHURCH! CANCEL THE RECEPTION!

WHAT? YOU'RE NOT GETTING MARRIED?

OF COURSE I AM! THIS IS FROM MY MAGAZINE. I'VE WON THE COMPETITION — SO THEY'RE FLYING US ALL OUT TO BARBADOS FOR THE WEDDING!

BARBADOS!

OH, KATE! THIS IS WONDERFUL!

And so —

BEING A BRIDESMAID IS GREAT FUN, AND THIS IS THE BEST HOLIDAY EVER! I'M THE LUCKIEST GIRL IN THE WORLD!

the end

What we really think about Mums and Dads!

PARENT

WE HATE! Parents who . . .

Say things were better when they were young.

Tell us we can't go out without a coat — then do it themselves.

Kiss us goodbye in front of mates!

Insist on picking us up after every disco.

Say we're too young to have pierced ears/eyebrows/noses!

Dress in 'young' clothes and think it makes them trendy.

Say, "we're more like friends than parent and child".

Expect us to join in their parties!

Think exams were harder when they were at school.

Hold hands and kiss — especially in public.

Tell us we have to be home by ten — even at the weekend.

Boast about us to their friends — especially if we're there!

Insist we eat all our vegetables!

Use 'cool' expressions.

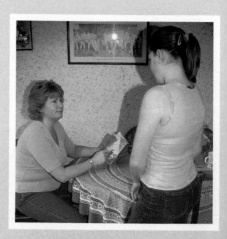

POWER!

WE LIKE! Parents who . . .

Let us choose our own clothes.

Tell us we're much cleverer than they were.

Never shop in our favourite shops.

Think computer games are educational.

Allow us to stay out late at weekends.

Pay our mobile phone bills without complaining.

WE LOVE!
Our parents — no matter what they say or do! (But, just in case you're reading this, Mum, can we have a little less of the soppy stuff, please?)

Don't embarrass us by asking silly questions at school parents' nights.

Keep out of our rooms (unless invited in to clean, of course!).

Give us pizza and burgers for every (well, almost every) meal.

Believe us when we tell them we've done our homework.

Realise that listening to CDs is just as important as piano practice.

Let us choose where to go on holiday.

Give us a TV in our room.

93

Continued from page 39

The Four Marys

WHILE on a school visit to Scotland, Mary Field was sure she had spotted a ghost. At lunch —

ER — WE WERE WONDERING, FIONA. DO — DO YOU HAVE ANY GHOSTS IN GLENAVERDALE HOUSE?

OH, YES! I'VE NEVER SEEN ANY MYSELF, BUT THERE ARE SUPPOSED TO BE QUITE A FEW.

WHAT? GH-GHOSTS IN THIS H-HOUSE!

DON'T WORRY, MABEL. THERE ARE NONE DOWNSTAIRS, WHERE YOU AND VERONICA ARE. ALL THE GHOSTS HAVE BEEN SEEN ON THE UPPER FLOORS.

THANK GOODNESS.

TCH! ENOUGH OF THIS NONSENSE. THERE ARE NO SUCH THINGS AS GHOSTS.

I WOULDN'T BE TOO SURE, MISS CREEF. THE SCOTTISH HIGHLANDS ARE SHROUDED IN SUPERNATURAL MYSTERY.

I THINK YOU'D BE BETTER CONCENTRATING ON SOMETHING SENSIBLE, FIONA — LIKE JOINING OUR NATURE WALK LATER.

So —

YOU'RE REALLY LUCKY TO LIVE HERE, FIONA. IT'S BEAUTIFUL.

YES — BUT LONELY AT TIMES. I'M USUALLY AWAY AT SCHOOL, BUT I CAME HOME EARLY BECAUSE YOU WERE COMING.

94

But —

TOO LATE! BUT — BUT LOOK AT THE WINDOW. IT WASN'T OPEN BEFORE . . .

WAIT A MINUTE!

LOOK AT THIS! IT'S A LITTLE VELCRO BUTTERFLY — FOR STICKING ON TRAINERS OR SOMETHING.

I KNOW WHO HAS SOME JUST LIKE THAT — AND *SHE'S* CERTAINLY NO GHOST!

OKAY, FIONA, YOU CAN SPILL THE BEANS. WHERE IS SHE? WE KNOW SHE'S HIDING SOMEWHERE.

YOU'RE RIGHT. THE GAME'S UP, MARY.

I STILL DON'T UNDERSTAND. WHAT GAME? WHO'S HIDING?

HI, GIRLS! SURPRISED TO SEE ME?

RADDY!

HA, HA, HA! YOUR BUTTERFLY GAVE YOU AWAY.

TCH! TRUST THAT TO FALL OFF. I COULD HAVE HAD GREAT FUN SCARING YOU LOT — WITH MY COUSIN, FIONA, HELPING, THAT IS.

LADY GLENAVERDALE IS MY AUNT AND I'VE BEEN GIVEN SPECIAL PERMISSION TO STAY HERE ALL WEEK — WITHOUT HAVING TO JOIN ANY OF CREEFY'S NATURE OR HISTORY CLASSES.

HUH! SOME PEOPLE HAVE ALL THE LUCK.

The days sped past and, eventually —

I CAN HARDLY BELIEVE IT'S OUR LAST DAY ALREADY, BUT AT LEAST IT'S ALL FREE TIME! WHAT D'YOU FANCY DOING, FIELDY?

HOW ABOUT A BOAT TRIP TO ONE OF THE ISLANDS?

NOT A GOOD IDEA, FIELDY. LOOK OUTSIDE!

OH, NO! THE RAIN'S COME ON! IT'S BEEN A GLORIOUS WEEK, BUT IT LOOKS LIKE OUR LAST DAY'S GOING TO BE A WASH OUT.

DON'T BE SO SURE. THERE ARE LOTS OF SECRET PASSAGES TO EXPLORE INSIDE. FIONA AND I WILL EACH TAKE A GROUP AND SHOW YOU A FEW.

So —

... AND THIS LEADS FROM THE OLD SERVANTS' QUARTERS IN THE ATTIC RIGHT DOWN TO THE KITCHEN. THE SERVANTS WOULD USE IT TO AVOID MEETING THE 'FAMILY'.

I SEE. AND ARE THERE HIDDEN DOORS INTO ANY ROOMS?

YEAH! INTO EVERY ROOM! THIS IS MY BEDROOM AND THE OPENING IS JUST LIKE THE ONE MARY — SORRY, RADDY — USED TO PLAY 'GHOSTS' IN YOUR ROOM.

COOL!

THAT EXPLAINS HOW RADDY DID HER FIRST DISAPPEARING ACT. THERE MUST BE A PANEL BEHIND THE DRAPES AT THE END OF THE CORRIDOR.

I WONDER HOW RADDY IS GETTING ON WITH THE OTHERS!

SCARING THEM SILLY, NO DOUBT!

And —

...SO, SILENTLY, THE MURDERER CREPT TOWARDS THE SECRET DOOR...

HA, HA, HA! YOU'RE MAKING THIS UP, RADDY.

IT'S REALLY HOT IN HERE. IT'S MAKING MY MIDGIE BITES ITCH.

MINE, TOO.

I'VE HAD ENOUGH. LET'S GO BACK. I'M SURE I'LL BE ABLE TO FIND A SHORTCUT.

WE-ELL — IF YOU SAY SO, MABEL.

Suddenly —

LOOK, MABEL! THE PANEL'S OPENING. YOU MUST HAVE HIT A SECRET CATCH.

AH, YES. I KNEW ALL ALONG THAT THIS WOULD BE A SHORT CUT.

GOODNESS, GIRLS! WHAT A NOISE! AND WHAT ON EARTH ARE YOU DOING SHUTTING YOURSELVES IN YOUR WARDROBE? IT'S LUCKY I WAS PASSING.

YES, MISS CREEF. SORRY, MISS CREEF.

But —

OH, NO! IT'S A DEAD END! HELP, SOMEONE! HELP!

But, as they stepped inside —

AARGH! WHAT'S HAPPENING? HELP!

SOMETHING TOUCHED MY FACE! WHAT IS IT? HELP! HELP!

98

YOU'LL BE PLEASED TO KNOW THAT THE WEATHER HAS CLEARED UP, SO WE'RE HAVING A BARBECUE ON THE ISLAND TONIGHT. WE'VE TIME TO PACK IN THE MORNING.

HUH! THERE'S NO WAY I'M GOING TO A STUPID BARBECUE TO GET EATEN ALIVE BY MIDGIES AGAIN. I'M PHONING DAD TO SEND THE HELICOPTER FOR ME *NOW!* DO YOU WANT TO COME?

YES, YES, *YES!* I CAN'T STAND THE THOUGHT OF *ONE* MORE BITE!

So, that evening —

THERE GO MABEL AND VERONICA. THEY DON'T KNOW WHAT THEY'RE MISSING.

YEAH! AND THE SMOKE FROM THE BARBECUE KEEPS THE MIDGIES WELL AWAY, SO NO ONE WILL GET BITTEN TONIGHT.

LET'S TELL GHOST STORIES.

OH, THAT REMINDS ME. IS THERE A SECRET PANEL BEHIND THE DRAPES AT THE END OF OUR CORRIDOR? YOU KNOW, WHERE YOU DISAPPEARED ON SUNDAY MORNING, RADDY.

NO — THERE'S NO SECRET PANEL THERE . . .

... AND I DIDN'T *GET* HERE UNTIL SUNDAY *AFTERNOON!* I ARRIVED JUST AFTER LUNCH, WHILE YOU WERE ON YOUR NATURE WALK WITH CREEPY.

SO — SO WHO WAS THE MAID I SAW IN THE MORNING?

Maybe they'd never know —

the end

Makeover Magic!

GREAT NEW LOOKS FOR MARIA!

funky!

Smart enough to wear for a trip into town or to the cinema, Maria jumped at the chance to try these jeans with their funky fringed belt. She chose a sweet sporty top to go with them and added groovy black boots for extra height! Finally, Maria's hair was pulled into funky bunches and tied with pink and purple baubles! Maria thought this outfit would be a cool look for wearing to the youth club.

oh, so soft!

This fluffy jumper made Maria ultra-cosy! She decided to wear it with pale brown cords and beige boots for an outfit she decided would be perfect for meeting friends in town. For a smart but simple look, Maria's hair was secured behind one ear with sparkly grips.

fab 'n' floaty!

Maria's favourite colour is light blue, so she pounced on this floaty top with shades of blue and lilac. For a special party look, Maria's hair was put up and held in place with a matching floaty bauble.

WHICH LOOK DID MARIA LIKE BEST? *"I'm going to buy the floaty blue and lilac top. I love it!"*

WAS THERE ANYTHING MARIA DIDN'T LIKE? *"I don't really like my hair in bunches – sorry!"*

The School Fete

DON'T make such a fuss. He was only sick over Alison once," said Zoe's mum, as she gently rocked Zoe's baby brother, Jack.

Zoe adored Jack, but he had an annoying habit of being sick, and now her mum was threatening to bring him to her school fete! It was just too much!

★ ★ ★ ★

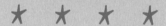

The day of the fete dawned and Zoe leapt out of bed to put on her costume. She was to be Madame La Mystere the gypsy. For 50p she would read palms or tell the future, wearing a fringed scarf, a sequinned skirt and false eyelashes.

When Zoe got to school, she was delighted to find her best friend, Lydia, had the stall next to her, where she would be face painting. To Lydia's left, Abigail was making flower crowns and, in the middle of the field, three girls were setting up a maypole.

"Where's your baby brother?" asked Lydia. "I'm dying to see him!"

"Oh, he's at home with a bit of a cold," fibbed Zoe. "Now, do you want your palm read?"

Lydia held out her hand and Zoe studied it carefully.

"Aha!" she said.

"Yes?" gasped Lydia.

But then a sudden wail stopped Zoe from saying any more.

★ ★ ★ ★

Oh, no! It couldn't be!

Zoe tried hiding behind her hand, but it was too late. Her mum came striding over to the stall, holding baby Jack triumphantly in the air.

"Darling," gushed Zoe's mum, "I've just seen Mrs Lowry and I haven't spoken to her in ages. Could you look after Jack for a minute?"

"But, Mum!" protested Zoe

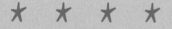

indignantly. "I can't do my fortune telling if I've to hold him!"

"Oh, Mrs Graham, what a lovely baby!" interrupted Lydia. "Can I hold him?"

Mrs Graham hesitated, but Zoe broke in, amazed at how possessive she suddenly felt.

"Don't worry, Mum. I'll do it."

Mrs Graham handed him over and made a dash for Mrs Lowry.

✱ ✱ ✱ ✱

Zoe started rocking her baby brother as Abigail rushed over, abandoning her flower stall.

"Oh, what a gorgeous baby! Can I hold him?"

"No, I want to," said Lydia, "I'm Zoe's best friend."

Zoe was startled to find that a crowd had gathered, all wanting to hold baby Jack. She felt tempted to start charging 50p a cuddle, but thought it might be a bit cheeky!

Despite all this attention, baby Jack didn't seem too happy and began to wriggle and cry.

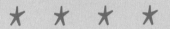

✱ ✱ ✱ ✱

"You're not holding him properly," said Lydia. "He'll choke if you hold him like that."

"Oh, don't be stupid!" snapped Zoe. "He's probably just got a bit of wind."

"But you're doing it all wrong," said Lydia. "Look, I know how to do it!"

She leaned forward to pick Jack up and, to everyone's surprise, he calmed down.

"I told you, didn't I?" said Lydia, looking smug.

However, her expression changed dramatically when Jack leaned forward and was sick all over Lydia's face paints.

Zoe laughed so much her sides hurt.

"So you know how to hold babies, do you?"

"Huh! You were rocking him too hard before you handed him over. Just look at this mess! I'm never speaking to you again!"

Just then Mrs Graham appeared and baby Jack began to smile.

"Thanks, girls! Enjoy the rest of your day!" she waved as she left.

But Zoe and Lydia stood at their stalls and ignored each other.

✱ ✱ ✱ ✱

Next day, Zoe crept in to school nervously. Lydia sat next to her in most lessons, and it would be awful if she ignored her.

As Zoe sat doodling baby faces on her book, she was surprised when Lydia came bounding over to her.

"You know what it's like having a baby in the family?"

"Yeah!" said Zoe quietly.

"Good! I'm going to need lots of advice," said Lydia, "My mum is having one in September."

Winter

FESTIVE FUN!

Cool crimbo puzzles for you!

YUM!

Here, the last letter of each answer is the first letter of the next answer and we've started you off with the first letter. Easy!

1. You begin a meal with this (7)
2. Oven-cooked vegetables (which can also be mashed or baked) (5,8)
3. This is put inside the turkey (8)
4. Brussels sprouts are this colour (5)
5. You'll need to crack these open to eat them (4)
6 A hot liquid served in a bowl (4)
7. Christmas, figgy or plum _ _ _ _ _ _ _ (7)

MISSING!

Add a letter to the beginning or end of each pair of words to make new words!

1. LOVE, OLD
2. PART, FAIR
3. TAR, NOW

TINSEL TANGLE!

Can you untangle these strands of tinsel? Which number goes with which letter?

A

B

C

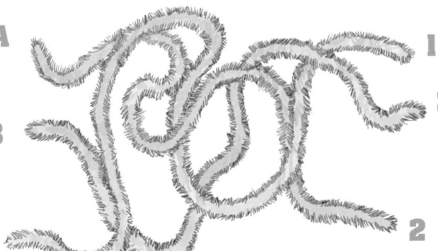

1

3

2

FESTIVE FUN!

U G R O
A O U F
F R O M
U F E R

G B A P
O D D A
A P G O
G D K P

COOL!

Score out the letters in your answers to the following questions and the letters which are left will spell out a winter bird – easy!

1. The colour of holly berries (3)
2. Wear this on your head (3)
3. A song sung at Christmas (6)
4. This'll keep your neck warm (5)

CRIMBO CROSSOUT!

Cross out the letters which appear more than twice in each present and you'll reveal two gift ideas!

ODD ONE OUT!

Which of these four Christmas tree scenes is different from the rest?

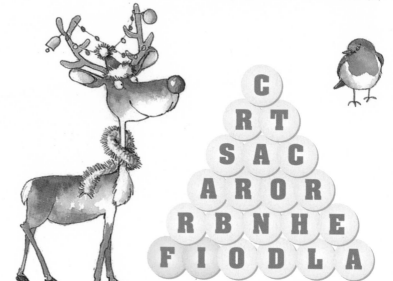

C
R   T
S A C
A R O R
R B N H E
F I O D L A

Find the following forty words hidden up, down, backwards, forwards or diagonally in this fab festive wordsearch! Letters can be used more than once.

ADVENT
ANGEL
BAUBLE

BELLS
BOOTS
BOW
BOXING DAY
CARDS
CAROL

CHRISTMAS
CINDERELLA
COOL
FAIRY
FROST
FUN

GLOVES
GOLD
GREEN
HAT
HOLIDAY
HOLLY
ICE
MISTLETOE
NOEL
PANTOMIME
PARTY
PRESENTS
PUDDING
RED
RIBBON
REINDEER
ROBIN
SANTA

C	A	R	O	L	L	E	O	n	A	H	B	G	J	I
H	A	T	R	F	S	E	M	I	M	O	T	n	A	P
R	S	A	n	E	E	R	G	B	W	L	H	C	n	E
I	T	R	C	A	I	T	K	C	H	L	L	O	G	O
S	O	E	D	B	S	E	C	I	O	Y	R	O	E	T
T	O	D	B	E	n	P	M	n	L	F	E	L	L	E
M	B	O	T	S	O	R	F	D	I	R	E	n	T	L
A	n	P	n	L	W	E	n	E	D	A	D	I	U	T
S	O	U	E	E	S	S	D	R	A	C	n	B	S	S
F	P	D	V	I	E	E	L	E	Y	S	I	O	L	I
U	A	D	D	G	V	n	O	L	E	T	E	R	L	M
n	R	I	A	H	O	T	G	L	T	U	R	K	E	Y
P	T	n	R	Q	L	S	B	A	U	B	L	E	B	V
S	Y	G	R	Y	G	Y	A	D	G	n	I	X	O	B

SCARF
SLEIGH
SNOW
STAR
TINSEL
TREE
TURKEY

ZZZZZ!

How many words of three letters or more can you make from these letters?

SLEEPING BEAUTY

Scores
25 - 30 FAIRY GOOD!
31 - 40 CHRISTMAS CRACKER!
41 + SANTA-STIC!

ANSWERS

113

You Say...

Just listen to what these cool chicks had to say when we asked them for some info!

Lauren

What's the nicest thing that's ever happened to you?

Lauren When I won my piano competition and got a trophy.

Emma I was performing in Whistle Down the Wind and I was asked to audition for the role of Brat!

Alice Joining the cast of Joseph and His Amazing Technicolour Dreamcoat.

Nicolle While on a school trip to Germany I visited a huge theme park with my best friends. I just didn't want the day to end.

Heather A few years ago my friends organised a surprise birthday party for me, and it was really cool. Thanks, guys!

Ashleigh Performing in Joseph and Whistle Down the Wind.

Heather

If you had £1000, how would you spend it?

Emma I'd visit New York and go to a Broadway Show.

Lauren I'd save £500 and blow the rest on a shopping spree.

Alice First I'd refurbish my bedroom, then I'd buy lots of clothes.

Ashleigh I'd buy clothes, CDs and DVDs.

Nicolle I'd put the money towards my trip to Mauritius.

Heather Some would go to charity, some would be saved and I'd spend the rest.

Alice

In which TV soap would you most like to appear?

Lauren EastEnders! Loads of people watch it, so they'd all see me!

Heather EastEnders, because it has the best plots and characters.

Nicolle Coronation Street. I think it has an amazing cast.

Alice I think Hollyoaks is the best soap of all, so that would be my choice.

Ashleigh It's Corrie for me.

Emma I like the storylines in Coronation Street, and I think it would be fun.

Nicolle

Who would you most like to meet – and why?

Ashleigh James Marsters, who plays Spike in Buffy. He's my idol.

Alice Orlando Bloom. I would like to ask him about the different movies he's been in.

Heather Justin Timberlake. He's really talented – and he's cool!

Emma Jennifer Aniston. I would ask her for beauty and acting tips.

Nicolle William Shakespeare, because he's the most amazing writer ever.

Lauren Justin Timberlake, because he's totally lush!

Ashleigh

What's your favourite thing in your bedroom?

Heather My TV.

Emma My double bed and American patchwork quilt.

Nicolle My bed.

Lauren My water feature.

Ashleigh My Spike poster.

Alice My lava lamp, cos it never looks the same twice.

Emma

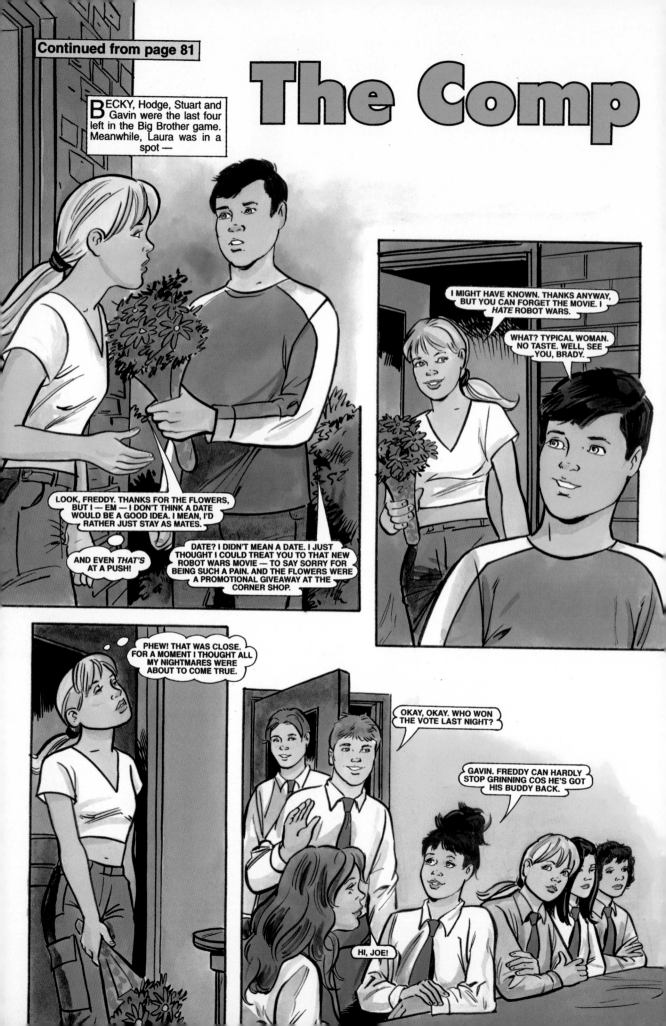

BUDGE OVER, HAYLEY. LET ME IN.

LOOK LIKES THAT FOUR ARE WELL SET UP NOW. I FEEL A BIT OF A SPARE PART.

CLAIRE AND I ARE GOING TO CLASS NOW, LAURA. WANNA COME ALONG WITH US?

WHAT? OH, YEAH, THANKS, NIKKI. I FEEL A BIT OF A GOOSEBERRY HERE.

YOU SHOULD CATCH THAT NEW ROBOT WARS FILM, LAURA. IT'S COOL. AND THE GUY IN IT LOOKS JUST LIKE BRAD PITT.

REALLY?

TYPICAL! I EVEN MISSED MY CHANCE OF *THAT*!

Meanwhile, in the domestic block —

THE GAME WILL BE JUST YOU AND ME SOON, BECKY. HOW ABOUT COMING OUT TONIGHT TO CELEBRATE?

NO TA. I'M WASHING THE DOG'S HAIR.

VERY FUNNY! IT'LL BE YOUR LOSS, TURNING DOWN THE CHAMPION.

DON'T PUSH YOUR LUCK! YOU COULD BE NEXT TO GO, YOU KNOW!

NO CHANCE. AND ADMIT IT, BECKY! YOU FANCY ME LIKE MAD!

ACTUALLY, I'M HERE TO TALK TO MY GIRLFRIEND — HAYLEY.

AND I'M WITH ROZ.

I DON'T BELIEVE THIS! I'M OUT OF CIRCULATION FOR FOUR DAYS AND EVERYTHING GOES PEAR-SHAPED!

STEVE AND JOE REALLY AREN'T TOO BAD, BECKY. NOTHING *LIKE* GAVIN!

MMM! IF YOU SAY SO, LAURA. I JUST WISH HAYLEY HAD TOLD ME. SOME SISTER SHE IS.

SHE PROBABLY DIDN'T WANT TO UPSET YOU — KNOWING HOW YOU FELT ABOUT GAVIN.

I SUPPOSE SO.

CHANGED YOUR MIND ABOUT THE CINEMA YET, BRADY? YOU CAN TREAT HODGE *AND* ME, IF YOU LIKE.

CINEMA? YOU? HODGE AND FREDDY? OH, *PLEASE*, LAURA, TELL ME THIS ISN'T HOW IT LOOKS.

IT ISN'T — I PROMISE — BUT IT'S A LONG STORY. I'LL TELL YOU ABOUT IT SOME TIME I HAVE A SPARE YEAR.

I'M GOING TO VOTE FOR GAVIN. HE'S GORGEOUS.

HUH! I WISH I COULD CHEAT AND PUT FIFTY VOTES IN FOR STUART. THIS MIGHT HAVE BEEN MY IDEA, BUT I NEVER DREAMED A PIG LIKE GAVIN MIGHT WIN.

I'M NOT SURE HE *WILL* WIN, BECKY. SOME GIRLS FANCY HIM, BUT JUST AS MANY CAN'T STAND HIM!

SORRY, STEVE, BUT STUART GETS MY VOTE THIS TIME. GAVIN'S JUST TOO SURE OF HIMSELF FOR MY LIKING.

THAT'S MORE LIKE IT, HAYLEY. GAVIN GREENE'S GOTTA GO!

DON'T SAY A WORD, BUT I'M VOTING FOR STUART, TOO. GAV'S A MATE AND ALL THAT, BUT HE'D BE UNBEARABLE IF HE WON.

COULDN'T AGREE MORE, MATE!

And —

YOU WILL BE PLEASED TO KNOW THAT OUR GAME HAS RAISED A RECORD AMOUNT OF MONEY FOR CHARITY. THE PATCHWORK QUILT HAS ALSO BEEN COMPLETED AND WILL BE HANDED OVER BY THE WINNER — STUART LINTON.

WELL DONE, STUART. YOU DESERVED TO WIN.

WHAT? IT'S A FIX! IT HAS TO BE. COME ON, LADS. I'M OUTTA HERE.

SORRY, GAV, JOE AND I ARE WALKING HOME WITH THE GIRLS.

EH? BUT WHAT ABOUT US? THE LADS?

WE'LL CATCH UP WITH YOU LATER, GAV.

WELL, LOOKS LIKE GAVIN'S BEEN PUT IN HIS PLACE AT LAST. HE WAS SO SURE HE'D WIN, HE EXPECTED ME TO GO OUT TO CELEBRATE WITH HIM TONIGHT.

WOULD YOU LIKE TO COME OUT AND CELEBRATE WITH ME, INSTEAD?

YEAH, STUART. I'D LOVE TO. BUT WHAT ABOUT LAURA? I HATE TO SEE HER ON HER OWN.

WELL, I COULD ALWAYS ASK MY BIG BROTHER TO COME ALONG AND MAKE UP A FOURSOME!

BIG BROTHER? *AAARGH!* I THINK I'VE HAD ENOUGH OF BIG BROTHERS FOR A WHILE — BUT I SUPPOSE IF IT'S FOR A MATE . . .

THAT'S THE SPIRIT, BECKY.

THIS GAME'S WORKED OUT EVEN BETTER THAN I'D HOPED! IT LOOKS LIKE I'M A WINNER AFTER ALL!

the end

120

Rosie Davenport was a sleepy head —

GET A MOVE ON, ROSIE, OR YOU'LL BE LATE FOR SCHOOL AGAIN!

WHAT? OH, SORRY, MUM!

YOU'LL HAVE TO START GOING TO BED EARLIER, ROSIE.

BUT I DO GO TO BED EARLY, MUM.

I JUST NEVER GET ENOUGH SLEEP!

Once Upon Another Time...

On the way to school Rosie met her friends, Fiona, Flora and Merry —

WHAT'S EVERYONE UP TO AT THE WEEKEND?

MERRY AND I ARE GOING OUT WITH STEVE AND MIKE.

AND I'M SEEING LEE.

WHY DON'T YOU COME ALONG AND MAKE UP A FOURSOME WITH LEE'S MATE, DARREN? HE REALLY LIKES YOU.

THANKS, FIONA, BUT I DON'T FANCY DARREN AND IT WOULD BE WRONG TO LET HIM THINK I DO.

TROUBLE IS, I DON'T FANCY ANYONE! I JUST WISH I DID.

BUT YOU'LL NEVER MEET ANYONE IF YOU DON'T GET OUT MORE, ROSIE.

MERRY'S RIGHT. YOU NEED TO FIND A HOBBY — OTHER THAN SLEEPING, THAT IS.

Later, Merry had an idea —

I'M GOING TO ASK ROSIE IF SHE'D LIKE TO JOIN OUR DRAMA GROUP. WHAT DO YOU THINK?

COOL! THERE ARE SOME NICE GUYS IN THE GROUP. MAYBE ROSIE'LL MEET SOMEONE SHE LIKES.

YEAH! WELL DONE, MERRY.

HUH!

Someone nearby didn't like the idea —

I'M NOT HAVING ROSIE DAVENPORT CHALLENGING ME! I'M THE LEADING ACTRESS IN THE GROUP! ME — MILLIE SKINNER.

Later the girls spoke to Rosie —

I'D LOVE TO COME ALONG. WHEN DO YOU MEET?

WEDNESDAYS. IN FACT, THERE ARE AUDITIONS FOR THE NEW PLAY NEXT WEEK.

YOU CAN BORROW MY SCRIPT TO LOOK AT THE PART.

GREAT, FIONA. THANKS A LOT.

A few days later —

I READ OVER THE SCRIPT LAST NIGHT, FIONA. DO YOU RECKON I COULD TRY FOR THE PART OF PRINCESS HELENA?

IT'S THE LEAD PART, BUT I DON'T SEE WHY NOT.

ADAM KING WILL PROBABLY GO FOR THE PART OF THE PRINCE. HE'S GORGEOUS, BY THE WAY. YOU'D LOOK REALLY GOOD TOGETHER.

IN YOUR DREAMS! I WANT THE PART OF HELENA — AND ADAM KING.

OH-OH! LOOKS LIKE MILLIE SKINNER DOESN'T FANCY THE COMPETITION. WE'D BETTER WATCH OUT FOR HER DIRTY TRICKS.

Sure enough, on the night of the audition —

THIS SHOULD MAKE SURE ROSIE BLOWS ANY CHANCE OF GETTING THE PART.

And soon —

ROSIE SAID SHE'D BE HERE BY NOW. MISS LAMBERT WANTS TO START.

I-I'LL GO TO MEET HER IF YOU LIKE. I'M NOT ON FOR AGES SO I WON'T MISS MY TURN.

And —

OH, THERE YOU ARE, ROSIE. THAT'S THE WAY TO THE STAGE — AND MISS LAMBERT IS WAITING.

TA, MILLIE.

But —

OH, BUT WHAT'S . . . AAAGH!

OH, DEAR. THE SIGN MUST HAVE BEEN WRONG. IT WAS THE PROPS CUPBOARD. ARE YOU OKAY?

YEAH, BUT I THINK I'VE GOT A SPLINTER IN MY FINGER. IF IT BLEEDS, I'LL FAI . . .

Rosie passed out. But —

I HEARD THE CRASH, MILLIE. IS SHE OKAY?

WHAT? OH — ER — SURE, ADAM!

OOH, WHAT HAPPENED?

WOW, WHO'S HE? HE'S GORGEOUS.

IT'S OKAY. YOU JUST FAINTED.

WOW! SHE'S FANTASTIC!

124

The End

Cool Colours!

If you were a colour, what would you be?
Our fun quiz reveals all!